MW00916497

Playing Catch
A Midwife's Memoirs

A Novel
Sally Urang

authorHOUSE™

1663 Liberty Drive, Suite 200
Bloomington, Indiana 47403
(800) 839-8640
www.AuthorHouse.com

Cover art by illustrationranch.com

Fish to Mammal

When a baby is born, takes its first breath, has its umbilical cord clamped, it changes from a fish to a mammal.

Whereas adult hearts are lopsided, with the fat, thick-walled left side acting as a stronger and more powerful pump than the weak, puny right side, the heart of a fetus is nearly symmetrical. It features little ducts and artificial openings and holes to shunt blood back and forth between the two sides in order to avoid circulating blood to the lungs, because fetal lungs are not yet capable of functioning. It is dedicated to providing a constant flow of a low-oxygen mixture to the brain, vital organs and nether parts.

An adult's heart, on the other hand, sends highly oxygenated blood to the brain and vital organs from the left side, while the right side circulates blood to the nearby lungs to obtain that oxygen.

So a fetus' plumbing is distinct from that of an adult, but miraculously able to change over in one extraordinary moment—the moment that the creature is born.

In that moment, the placenta, which has acted as a giant set of gills for all that time, becomes a minor player, a temporary organ that has outlived its usefulness. The lungs, which were filled with fluid and resistant to circulation, expand, replace the fluid with air and welcome the flow of blood. The ducts and holes that used to bypass critical parts of the heart's outflow vessels snap shut and seal over as the baby breathes for the first time, allowing oxygen-rich blood to nourish its brain, kidneys, liver, stomach and other essential parts.

Now the baby, too, has an asymmetrical heart. Rather quickly, his hard-working left pump will become more muscular and stronger than his smaller, weaker right pump.

This is why delivering a baby is never a casual thing. No matter how irreligious the circumstances, no matter how tired I am, no matter what profanities have been flung, the birth of a baby represents a phenomenon of physiology not witnessed by ordinary mortals.

So midwifery is an experience of transcendence. It is sometimes hard to remember this when a patient whines nonstop for four hours, or when her mother is parked in a chair cackling at Jerry Springer while the patient howls in pain, or when the patient grabs my arm and tries to wrestle me onto the bed during a contraction, or calls me a liar or a butcher.

Sometimes the baby's head begins to cry before its body is delivered. Here's a little slimy head looking around, making noise, waiting for its body to be born. And all the while a physiologic miracle is taking place inside that baby's chest.

Sometimes a baby is born with lungs too immature or diseased to function as mammalian lungs. The baby tries to keep being a fetus, even though it is now outside the womb and its placenta is in a red plastic bucket marked "Hazardous Waste." The lungs remain a high-pressure zone, the right side of the heart continues to shunt blood to the left side, and all the artificial holes and ducts stay open. The baby has been born and needs to evolve, but it recognizes, on the most visceral level, that it is not yet fit to be a mammal. If only it could get that placenta back!

Twice in my life I have shaken hands with babies not yet born. In both cases, the fetuses had *compound presentations*—a hand was alongside the head, instead of tucked against the chest. In both cases, my fingers touched fetal fingers.

In the first case, the fetus' tiny finger touched my finger and then rapidly pulled away, as though shocked or repelled by my touch. I, too, was shocked, and pulled my fingers back slightly, only realizing seconds later what I had felt.

In the second case, the fetus seemed curious, and its fingers stroked, caressed and explored my examining fingers. Its touch was feathery, yet substantial.

I was amazed. I was conversing, in some sense, with someone who was not yet born—who would not be born for hours, perhaps days. I felt as people must feel who have had alien encounters. It happened, yes, and it will always be a significant experience, but there is almost no one with whom I can share the memory.

Attending a birth is a religious experience. This is yet another reason why modern obstetrics, with its insistence on turning the birth of a person into a tense, high-decibel surgical procedure, is deeply flawed. There should be joy, there should be reverence, there should be awe and wonder, not terror, not dread, not impatience.

Unfortunately, if you attend enough births, something terrible will surely happen to take away your innocent joy. That's just the way it is. No matter how good you are, how smart you are, how hard you keep studying and learning, how meticulous you are, how high a standard you maintain for your own practice, something terrible will happen. It's only a matter of time. And all the joy you felt at the beginning will fade away, to be replaced with doubt and fear.

You will go through massive changes. You will relive the experience over and over, trying to turn the clock back, start again and make everything right. You will review everything you did and said and thought, to see where you made the mistake. Chances are, you will realize you didn't make a mistake. Terrible things happen some-times, usually for no reason at all.

I have a photograph that a patient gave me once, years ago. I have long since forgotten the patient's name, the circumstances, or the timing. The picture is of me, in a paper surgical gown and gloves, my hair illuminated by the high-intensity overhead light, triumphantly holding a newborn baby aloft. The baby is still dripping wet and slimy, not even a minute old.

My face is flushed and shiny with sweat. My hair is slightly longer than it is now, I can tell that it's summer outside, and the look on my face is one of pure joy. I am saying something to the camera, but I cannot recall what it is.

I am so happy.

I need to get that back.

How did I get here?

Part One

Hygiene/Elimination

Holy shit!

I glanced at the floor of the shower stall. Could it be? Were those really—? Had the old man gotten his activities confused? This was supposed to be "Hygiene," not "Elimination."

My charge, a Mr. Dupree, silenced by a long-ago stroke, had apparently no idea that the shower was not the same as the toilet. What was I supposed to do now?

What on earth was I doing?

I had asked myself this question countless times since six months before, when I left my comfortable career as an editor for a prestigious daily newspaper —*the* daily newspaper—to become a certified nurse-midwife. Something in me yearned for a satisfaction that journalism —copyediting, to be specific—could not provide. But this? Witnessing a helpless, mute old man ravaged by disease taking a crap in a shower stall? What did this have to do with my career path? I was sup-posed to deliver babies, for God's sake.

I was reasonably content at the New York Daily Banner. My job was challenging and occasionally rewarding. I hung out with smart, funny, sarcastic people. I made a great salary, which allowed me to take expensive vacations, eat lunch out every day, go shopping regularly for clothes and shoes, and get my hair dyed professionally. Still I fanta-sized about a life in which I would have a more direct effect on people. In the United States, until recently, in order to be a certified midwife, you must become a registered nurse first.

So here I was, hosing down Mr. Dupree, ask-ing myself if I'd lost my mind.

"Uh-uh-uh-uh-*UHHHNNNNHH!*"   Mr. Dupree yanked on my white polyester top, star-ing at the floor of the shower stall and grunting.

He pointed with a gnarled finger to the of-fending objects that had shocked me only seconds before.

" U h - u n h h h - *U N H H H H - u h -UNNNHHHHHH!*" His finger, trembling slightly, moved closer to the objects, as if to inspect them. He was bent nearly double in the shower chair, a nifty advanced-yoga pose.

"No, no, Mr. Dupree," I said. "Don't you both-er. I've got this."

I grabbed the shower-hose attachment and aimed a fine spray at the trio of turds. I slid Mr. Dupree's chair back a foot, out of turds' way. Sure enough, the water gun was beginning to break up the forbidden objects. If I adjusted the fineness of the spray, I discovered, I could actually force small bits down the drain.

Reassured, Mr. Dupree settled in to watch me. I stood away from the stream of water, in a fencer's stance, to avoid back spray.

With patience and a steady hand, I was able to wash away any trace of the giant boo-boo. So there you go! The day wasn't a total waste after all! I had learned a wholly new skill!

Triumphant, I toweled Mr. Dupree off and put him in a fresh gown, in the ass-loving style favored by hospitals and nursing homes, "open to the back."

"Ready to roll, Mr. D?" I asked.

I wheeled him to his room, transferred him to his "geri-chair," and wheeled him back to the day room, where my nursing-school colleagues and my lovely instructor, Darlene Sklar, awaited. The emergency turd-removal had taken a tad longer than I had planned, and I was late for "post-conference."

"There you are, Sarah," Darlene said. "We had almost given up on you. Did you fill out the daily summary?"

"Not yet, Darlene," I said. "We had a little setback. I'm sorry to be late."

"A setback! Is everything all right?"

"Oh, yes, everything's peachy." I shot a glance at my friend Moe. She was the only one in this late-adolescent group who understood me, and vice versa.

Despite our obvious older age in comparison with our first-year classmates at The New York College of Arts and Sciences (Ivy League!) School of Nursing, Moe and I were expected to be as naïve, starry-eyed and idiotic as they.

Darlene Sklar, assistant dean and director of the surgical nursing program, had strongly advised me six months earlier to abandon my adult status and return to adolescence, for the good of my studies.

"I see that you live on West Eleventh Street," she said, looking out at me from behind coke-bottle glasses. Her office had a strange, not unpleasant odor of stale Velveeta. Her hair was an indescribable color; sort of purplish-green, and her face bore the pockmarked remnants of the most severe kind of cystic acne sometime in her youth. Her secret nickname among the more cynical students at NYCAS was "Hank." (I had coined this unfortunate epithet. This was because Darlene bore an uncanny resemblance to my ex-boyfriend Hank—not a good-looking man, mind you.)

"Yes, I do!" I said, trying to read upside-down the contents of the folder on her desk bearing my name.

"You should move into the dorm," she said.

"I beg your pardon?"

"You should really make arrangements to move into the dorm. It'll be better."

"Are you saying that I have to live in the dorm?" I queried, panic-stricken.

"No, Sarah, but it'll be much better for you. For one thing, you'll be closer to the main campus and most of the clinical sites. For another, you'll be able to form study groups with the other nursing students."

"I'm sorry, Hn—"—I actually started to address her as Hank— "—arlene"— it came out "'H'n'arlene"—"I can't possibly live in the dormitory."

"Why not, Sarah? It's very affordable. You'll probably save a lot of money, actually."

"No, no, you don't understand. I'm an *adult*. I can't live in a *dorm*."

"Why not?"

"You see, I'm not a kid in my twenties like some of these guys. I'm an *adult*."

"I fail to understand the problem with the dorm."

"Darlene, I'm an *adult*. I'm—you know, like, you know, *sexually active*. I had a *career* before. I, like, paid *bills*. I *gave parties*. I *own furniture*. Do you understand?"

"Well, yes, Sarah, I recognize that you're older than most of the students, but I still think the dorm would be a good idea."

"Why don't I think about it, then, eh?"

"That'll be fine, then, dear. Now, let's talk about that statistics requirement. I think you should take it pass-fail, don't you?"

Now, six months later, still living in my rent-controlled West Village apartment, I had steadfastly resisted the urge to become an adolescent again, although the pull was there, and strong as an industrial magnet. In my clinical group the mean age (excluding Moe and me) was 22. It would have been a short hop to find myself puffing up my bangs with a round brush, some gel and a blow-dryer, or appearing at my next-door neighbor's in my nightgown for a late-night Jiffy Pop and girl-talk session (except that my next-door neighbor was 73 and had a service dog). Had I discovered that I was now subscribing to *Tiger Beat* and *Seventeen*, I would not have been a bit surprised. I was surrounded by the Young and the Clueless—all day, every day.

There in the day room of the nursing home, I stared at their bright, empty faces. They in turn stared at Darlene. Outside the smeary picture window, in the bright sunshine, an urban bird, a house finch, was singing frenetically. I loved them: their "kinda-red" feathers, their cheekiness, their boldness, their tuneless, frantic melodies, each one different from the next and last, like snowflakes. Could no one else hear it?

"Quickly, Sarah, fill out the daily summary and let's discuss our experiences."

Hmmmm… *"Nutrition:"*—I could by now barely recall dining with Mr. D., given our most recent adventure. Oh, yes! He had spat a wad of it square onto the front of my white polyester smock earlier in the day.

"You're feeding him too fast," the supervising nurse had admonished me. It's true, I had not put one hundred percent of myself into the task; the fact was, "All My Children" was playing in the lunch room and I was trying to unravel the latest intrigue between Erika and Dmitri when I really should have been paying attention to Mr. D's green slop.

"*Something puréed,*" I scribbled. (I was proud of myself for remembering the *accent aigu.*)

"*Hygiene:*"—that was easy. "*Long hot soapy shower!*" I wrote enthusiastically.

"*Activity:*"—this could be tricky. Strictly speaking, we hadn't had an activity, because the "hygiene" component of our day had been so labor-intensive. *What the hell,* I thought. I wrote, "*Chased turds in shower.*"

"*Elimination:*"—I wrote, "*See above.*"

"Here you are, Darlene."

She glanced at the paper. Her face fell as she read my comments, her lips sticking on her upper teeth as a dog's sometimes do. She turned an angry purple color, the pockmarks standing out in ghastly relief—almost fluorescent—against the rapidly filling blood vessels in her forehead and cheeks.

"No, Sarah, this *will not do!*"

"Why do you torment her?" Moe asked me later, as we walked towards the subway together.

"Don't you want to graduate from this scum-sucking hell-hole so you can go to midwifery school?"

She had a point. It couldn't possibly further my career goals to provoke Hank all the time. At any rate, she had gotten the big picture when I had explained to my group in graphic detail how Mr. D. had let his sphincters relax in the warm shower, and how much it had disturbed him to see his fecal material lying there.

"That's why I was late, Darlene. I had to clean it up and calm him down," I said with absolute sincerity. She was not entirely impressed, however, and I had to agree to rewrite the daily summary overnight, using that mind-numbing nursing jargon Hank loved so much, and adding insignificant details until she was satisfied.

It was just as Moe had observed: The study of nursing was all about inflating pointless minutiae into enormous tomes, as though you took a copy of "Goodnight Moon" and blew into it until it was as big as the Oxford English Dictionary.

And that, dear reader, was *only the first day!*

Lucky Buddha

Moe and I decided that we had to get laid. As nursing students, our lives were unbelievably unglamorous—anti-glamorous, really— so depressing, so emotionally draining, filled with one tedious, foul-smelling chore after another.

And just try telling a group of adults at a cocktail party, "I'm a nursing student," and watch what happens.

Our self-esteem was suffering, we were broke, we wore 100 percent polyester 50 percent of the time, and we were the social equivalent of lepers. The only thing that could possibly salvage the smoldering wreckage of our lives was regular sex. Affordable, entertaining, calorie burning and good for the soul.

"How are we going to do this?" Moe asked.

"I have an idea," I said. We were chatting on the phone late one Sunday night.

"But first, the incantation," I insisted.

We were knee-deep in our six-week surgical nursing rotation, and both of us had "clinical" the next day—eight exhausting hours of smelling heretofore unimagined odors, slipping in body fluids, peeling dressings off wasted flesh and generally finding new and ever more horrifying ways to test our gag reflex, all beginning at 7 a.m.! Moe's "experience" was taking place at St. Adele's Hospital in the Bronx, famous for drive-by shootings, while mine unfolded Monday through Friday at the NYCAS Medical Center in Washington Heights, the "Mecca," the true House of God, the teaching hospital to end all teaching hospitals.

Nightly, Moe and I lit our "Lucky Buddha" candles and prayed the "trache prayer":

Oh, Lord Buddha, creator of all good things, may I not suction a trache tomorrow.

Moe had purchased her Lucky Buddha candle in Chinatown, and it thoughtfully provided an English translation on one side of the glass:

Oh, Lucky Buddha, send me your luck. Happiness, love, money. Good fortune!

My Lucky Buddha candle, on the other hand, was picked up in Washington Heights, where Lord Buddha speaks Spanish:

Senor Buda de la suerte, da me su suerte. Felicidad, el amor, y el dinero. Fortuna buena!

"Are you lighting it?" Moe asked.

"Okay, repeat after me:"

(We both intoned) *Oh, Lord Buddha, creator of all good things, may I not suction a trache tomorrow.*

A "trache" (pronounced "trake") is a tracheotomy—a surgical hole cut in someone's throat when his or her upper airway, or *trachea*, no longer connects to his or her lower airway (or *lungs*). Examples of this situation include throat cancer, severe asthma causing the airways to shut down, or an extreme allergic reaction causing the throat to swell. A "trache" could be permanent or temporary, depending on the situation that necessitated it.

After the hole is cut, a tube is placed in the hole that opens out to the great outdoors. There is an inner tube that is removable, and when it is removed, thick snotty secretions must be suctioned out of the trache-hole/tube. If the thick snotty secretions are not suctioned on a regular basis, the trache can become clogged and the person sporting it can die.

Suctioning a trache is not only intensely gross. It is also scary. Because you are temporarily removing the patient's ability to breathe, you must be totally ready to perform the procedure; you must keep the patient calm; you must give him an extra helping of oxygen before and after, and you must work quickly, all the while being calm, pleasant and reassuring.

The need to vomit in mid-procedure could possibly hinder you from carrying out this task capably. Some of the Young & Clueless sharing our surgical "experience" had told horror stories in post-conference, and suctioning traches had thus become a kind of mythical rite of passage:

If you could do it and both you and the patient survived, you'd probably make it through the rest of the program. Moe and I had independently arrived at the conclusion that we would never need to suction a trache as midwives, and we wanted no part of it.

I decided to go further than just chanting.

That night before I fell asleep, I prayed:

"God, if you just see to it that I won't have to suction any traches during nursing school, I promise to take care of poor women for the rest of my life."

I knew in my heart this was wrong. You couldn't just ask God for favors when it was convenient. Plus, what if God gave me what I asked for, and I tried to renege on my offer later?

Anyway, back to my idea for getting laid. The Museum of Natural Sciences, of which I was a longstanding member, offered regular weeknight lecture series.

"So what's the point?" Moe asked.

"*Men* attend lectures!"

"What makes you so sure?"

She had me there.

"Well, it's better than doing nothing. Maybe we'll learn something. It's only one night a week for four weeks. If we hate it, if there are no men, if it's boring, we'll go drinking instead. And it's free!"

"How can we optimize our chances of meeting men at these lectures?" Moe wanted to know.

"Well," I said thoughtfully, "how about if we choose the most *manly* lecture they offer?"

We decided that "Cro-Magnon Man: Our Link to the Past" offered the best hope of attracting men.

It turned out to be unnecessary.

The very day after "Cro-Magnon Man: Our Link to the Past: Part I," I met a man and *so did Moe!*

Odd-Job

So, you may wonder, how did two unemployed nursing students survive through two long years of nursing school?

We both had rent-stabilized apartments. Moe borrowed from her mother and I sold my Daily Banner stock and used virtually all of my savings. We sometimes baby-sat on weekends; I pet-sat and dog-walked for people in my building, and Moe ran errands for an art gallery in SoHo from time to time where her mother had once worked. My friend Rose, who didn't make that much money herself (she was an assistant district attorney in the Bronx), had vowed to take me out for a cheap dinner once a week as long as I was in nursing school, which saved about $10 a week.

And the Odd-Job helped a lot.

The Odd-Job is a store on Fourteenth Street and University Place. Three stories of discounted everything. Cat litter—99 cents a bag ($3.99 a bag for a similar brand elsewhere)! Scotch tape —99

16

cents for six rolls! Ironing board covers of every description—$2.99! Spatulas, 99 cents! Chocolate turtles, 12 cents each! Hershey's kisses, 59 cents a bag! Potting soil, 39 cents a bag. Fiddle-Faddle *or* cheese corn, take your pick—69 cents a bag! And best of all, not Kraft, but *Kraft-like* macaroni and cheese—33 cents a box! That's *three dinners for a buck*, people!

"What a deal!" I swung my giant Odd-Job bag fore and aft as Moe and I walked back towards Moe's place, a song in our hearts. It was getting dark. The air was cold, and there was a wonderful smell in the air of roasted peanuts and cigarettes and garlic.

In her living room, we poured out the contents of our bags. Moe had six boxes of Kraft-*like*, two turtles, two Fiddle-Faddle, a pack of three generic vac bags for $1.25, six rolls of Scotch tape, three pairs of cotton panties (69 cents on special!), a "Maybelle" (Maybelline-*like*) pressed powder, a quart of "Clairette" shampoo (Clairol-*like*), generic cream rinse, two bags of cat litter and an ironing board cover. Total price: $27.13!!

My bags featured two cat litters, four turtles, two bags of cheese corn, six Kraft-*like*, roll-on deodorant, 25 Bic-*like* ballpoint pens ($3!!), one ironing board cover, a quart of "Clairette," three pairs of tube socks (two bucks!), three panties, a quart of generic dill halves ($2.99), a tub of crunchy peanut butter (99 cents!), three loose-leaf notebooks for 99 cents, a case of generic cat food ($5.99!!!), and generic beer (12 for $5.99). Total price: $40.08!!!

On days when we had "clinical experiences," we skipped breakfast and waited, like vultures, until about 10:30 a.m., when uneaten breakfast trays (hard-boiled eggs and Rice Krispies) became available. That amounted to a saving of up to four dollars, when you think about it.

On days when we didn't have clinicals but early classes, I had leftover, reheated coffee and toast with butter, standing at the counter of my dark kitchen at 6:30 a.m. Moe and I made a solemn vow: As long as we were this poor, we didn't waste anything, not leftover coffee, not even the heels of bread. Moe used to gather up the scraps of soap in her soap dish, melt them in her microwave and fashion them into a new bar of soap. In this way, she avoided buying soap for months at a time.

Lunch we ate in the hospital or nursing school cafeteria—the salad bar. If you got lots of lettuce with dressing, extra saltines and hardly any olives or heavy stuff, you could get away with a hearty lunch for about two dollars. And it was good for you, too.

Dinner was always the same: A half-box of Kraft-like, dill halves, fiddle-faddle or cheese popcorn, generic beer.

In this way we lived on very little.

Colostomy Care

It was Friday afternoon. I had had an exciting day on my surgery rotation. No traches, but to pay me back for my irreverence, God had given me "colostomy care."

A colostomy is another artificial hole, this one surgically placed in the intestine and opening out of the abdomen to a plastic bag glued to a person's belly. When someone suffers, say, a gunshot wound to the abdomen that affects the bowel, or cancer of the colon, or some terrible obstruction of the bowel, a colostomy becomes necessary to remove solid waste. Like a trache, a colostomy may be permanent or temporary.

Mrs. G., a tiny, ancient woman with advanced colon cancer who had just had an operation to remove the cancerous bowel, was my charge for that Friday. For the past four days, I had listened as the nurses on the post-surgical ward described Mrs. G. in morning report.

"S.G., an 84 year old black female, is

> *status post hemi-colectomy for Stage
> II colon cancer. She is DNR..."* [the
> hospital abbreviation for "do not
> resuscitate" — a decision made by
> the patient and/or family when
> the patient's condition is terminal.
> This meant that if Mrs. G. suffered
> a cardiac arrest or stopped breath-
> ing, the staff would do nothing to
> resuscitate her.]
>
> *"... Her colostomy is not productive
> yet. She is tolerating a soft diet. She is
> getting Cefazolin two grams IVSS q 6
> hours; she is afebrile and her dressing is
> dry and intact. She needs daily dressing
> changes."*

By Thursday, as I listened to this exact same
info, I began to wonder: Shouldn't Mrs. G's colostomy be "productive" by now? After all, the surgery was last Friday and she had been on a soft
diet for three whole days.

Day after day, the nursing students rotated
through Mrs. G., until it was my turn that Friday.

Mrs. G. was not very chipper. Our day began
with me feeding her breakfast at 8 a.m. I tried to
talk quietly to her while I was feeding her, as I
had seen the nurses do.

"Well, it may snow today," I said as I spooned
up the oatmeal and pushed it into her mouth. I
recalled my experiment with Mr. Dupree at the
nursing home; how I'd fed him too fast and he had

rewarded me by spitting a big wad of something green onto my uniform top.

"Am I going too fast, Mrs. G?"

"Feeling sick. Not hungry."

"Oh, but Mrs. G, you've gotta eat. You just had an operation. You need nourishment to heal. Come on, take another bite."

"Don't want it. Too full. Leave me alone. Gonna throw up."

Indeed, she attempted to sit up in bed and appeared agitated, groping the sheets with her wizened hands. This was all I needed—to be vomited on so early in the day.

Something told me to examine her colostomy bag to see if it was "productive." Staring at the manufacturer's logo on the bag, I noticed a clear plastic disk over the opening. The opening was covered. Could this be the reason the colostomy was not "producing"?

I felt my heart pounding. What if I was wrong? But Mrs. G really seemed to be in acute distress, as we say.

"Stay here! I'll be right back!" I told her. *(Where did I think she was going to go?)*

I ran into the hall. Where in the hell was Hank?

At this point in our relationship, Hank/Darlene barely tolerated me. After all, I had steadfastly refused to move into the dorm with the Y&C, I was known for my constant, involuntary eye rolling in lecture and post-clinical conference, and the word on the street was that I had "an attitude." Of course, anyone whose brains hadn't been previously sucked out through their ears would suffer from involuntary constant eye rolling and "attitude" in nursing school. It was such a continuous crock of shit.

For example, there was "nursing diagnosis." Medical diagnosis, or "differential diagnosis," is straightforward and fairly easy to grasp. You listen to the patient's "chief complaint," you order some tests, you perform a physical exam, ask some probing questions about the patient's current condition, and you decide which things you think it could be. (It's usually more than one thing that you think it could be.)

For example, someone comes into the E.R. with belly pain and a fever "times two days." (That's how we say it, in medical talk: "fever times two days." You write it: "Fever X 2d".) You talk to him about the nature of the pain, when it started, what relieves it, what makes it worse, what he's eaten lately, has he had a poop, does he have an appetite, etc. You check his *vital signs* (temperature, pulse, blood pressure and respiratory rate), *palpate* (feel with your fingers and hands) his belly, maybe even *percuss* (tap on your own splayed-out fingers over his belly to hear what the tissue underneath sounds like), check his urine for protein, white blood cells, red blood cells, glucose and other substances, order some blood work, and come up with a *differential diagnosis, viz.*:

Rule out acute appendicitis
Rule out small bowel obstruction.

Rule out *peritonitis* (inflammation of the lining of the lower abdomen). Later on, your more elaborate tests—or exploratory surgery—will confirm which of the things it is, *ruling out* the other possibilities, and you will treat him accordingly.

But nursing is a separate discipline from medicine. Perhaps because of years of being looked down upon by doctors, the people who make up the rules of nursing have gone to great pains to make clear just how separate the two professions are. A needless arrogance informs these rules, sometimes to nursing's detriment. It is as though nurses want to avoid, at all costs, being mistaken for doctors.

We are nurses. Not doctors. Separate, but equal.

We are just as good as doctors and just as smart, but we're completely different. We have our own way of looking at health care—not a doctor's way, but just as valuable.

Therefore, nursing cannot align itself with anything that smacks of medicine and doctors, even if it's something good, time-tested and convenient, like medical diagnosis. Borrowing from doctors' lingo might blur the lines between us and them, and also might make communication between us easier.

We can't have that!

Also, nursing looks at the whole person, not just the disease. A good idea in principle, but this can be taken to ridiculous levels. There is no *disease* in nursing, there are only *alterations in the normal*.

So instead of just writing, "He has a gunshot wound to the aorta and is bleeding out," you must write, *"Alteration in hemodynamic function related to injury."*

Someone who had a hemi-colectomy for cancer and now has a colostomy has an *"Alteration in elimination (bowel) related to disease process."*

The absurdity of this oblique way of describing straightforward conditions would soon be beautifully illuminated in our Psych rotation, in which a floridly schizophrenic patient who thinks the nursing student looks like a giant saddle shoe is experiencing an *"Alteration in perception (visual) related to disease process."* A doctor would just say, "He's fucking crazy."

My contempt for nursing diagnosis was legendary. I had actually described once, in a paper, a patient with end-stage renal disease as having an "alteration in elimination (urinary) related to fried beans." (Fried beans was medical slang for kidney failure. The kidneys are *beans*, you see, and when they go, they are "fried.")

Hank was suitably disdainful of me by now, but I had a straight-A average, so she couldn't say much.

"Darlene! I think there's something wrong with my patient's colostomy!"

She looked up warily. She was helping another student, one of the Y&C, do a wet-to-dry-dressing.

"I mean it. I think it's blocked. She's in some kind of distress."

Reluctantly, Hank accompanied me to Mrs. G's room.

"See? What *is* that?" I pointed out the clear plastic disk in the hole in Mrs. G's belly.

"How can the colostomy produce with that there?"

Hank was concerned.

"They're not supposed to make the caps in clear plastic," she said. "They're supposed to be a different color so you can see them. *They used to be blue!* Hand me some gloves and *stand back!*"

As Hank removed the bag and the disk from Mrs. G's colostomy hole, a long, firm snake of shit began to shoot out of it like those fake worms that kids squirt out of aerosol cans. Hank tried valiantly to scoop the shit into a chux pad, but it kept coming and coming, arcing up into the air at times before it broke into pieces. Soon it was on the floor, on the side of the bed, everywhere. All we could do was stand back and watch. Four days of a soft diet had backed up practically to Mrs. G's throat.

So all the nurses and the Y&C who had taken care of Mrs. G. for the past week had failed to see that the company that makes the colostomy bags had changed the color of the caps from blue to clear, thus making it difficult to notice that Mrs. G's artificial pooper was completely blocked. Hence the lack of "productivity," her poor appetite, her nausea, etc.

"Boy! No wonder you didn't feel good, Mrs. G!" I shouted.

"You bet!" Mrs. G. cracked. I wouldn't have been surprised if, at that very moment, she had burst into an *a cappella* chorus of "I Shall Be Released."

Hank eyed me suspiciously.

"How did you notice it?"

"Well, I kept wondering why the nurses kept saying, 'her colostomy is not productive yet; her colostomy is not productive yet,' and days had gone by. Then today she was really reluctant to eat. So I just took a look at it and saw that thing."

After the mess was cleaned up, Mrs. G felt much better and so did I. I had experienced my first *bed change (occupied)*, as Hank and I chatted and bonded while rolling Mrs. G from side to side and enfolding the shitty sheets into foul, flat little parcels. We sprayed the room down with some sort of flower-garden-in-a-can, plumped Mrs. G's pillow, washed her nether parts and had a rip-roaring good time. Mrs. G., unclogged, reverted once again to her true self: gossipy, giggly and good-natured.

Hank was clearly thrilled. She'd have a story for the next faculty meeting, for sure!

"Sarah, your observation skills saved that patient's life," she said outside the room. By this time, word of the unclogged shitter had spread throughout the surgical floor. A couple of nurses, two medical students and a senior surgical resident had shown up during the cleanup phase to behold the poop-snakes everywhere.

"Naw," I said.

"You really did," said a male voice behind me.

I turned to face a moderate- to-severely gorgeous man wearing green scrubs, the "vee" of the shirt of which revealed a suitable quantity of chest hair (a look I found irresistible in those days). He had broad shoulders, sandy-brown curly hair and a big smile. He looked to be fairly young and fresh, probably an intern. I stared open-mouthed.

"Good work," he said, and disappeared.

Hank was so enamored of me that she stayed glued to me until the lunch break, helping me change Mrs. G's dressing and generally smooching my ass.

After the lunch break, Hank said, "I think you've had enough excitement for one day. Why don't you ask the nurses for the manicuring equipment and give Mrs. G a manicure for the rest of the shift? I'll pass your meds for you."

What a deal! You free up a week's worth of shit, you get to take the afternoon off! Mrs. G and I had a fine old time, watching "the stories" on ABC, cackling, gossiping about her family members and getting her nails in tip-top condition. I got to hear about her worthless nephew, Clive, who was trying to get hold of Mrs. G's life savings by claiming that she had promised it to him in a sort of oral will.

"Well, Mrs. G.," I had advised her solemnly, "You'd best get your daughter to bring a lawyer up in here ASAP and get your real will re-signed and notarized."

Of course, I was the hero of post-conference, and got to smile bashfully while Hank told the group the whole shitty story, making it into a sort of parable about how observation by an astute nurse can save a patient's life.

"Day after day, Sarah heard those nurses saying that Mrs. G's colostomy was 'not yet productive,' and instead of just nodding and writing it down, Sarah thought to ask *'why not?'*"

(I still don't know whether Mrs. G. might have actually died of chronic shit backup. It sounds fishy to me.)

But now it was 5:30 p.m., and I was settling into my end-of-the-week glazed-over phase. I had forgotten to return the manicuring equipment, so I went to the utility room to put it back. I had completely fried the lone brain cell that held the combination to the lock on the utility-room door. I stood there, eyes closed, swaying back and forth slightly, trying to empty my mind so I could recall the combination.

"You locked out?"

I turned to face the same guy from earlier. Still smiling, still gorgeous, still with the lovely, lovely, lovely chest hair peeking out. I fantasized combing through his chest hair with my fingers. *(We'd be sweaty, of course, and naked, and I'd be half-draped across him in a small, dark room with only a ceiling fan to cool us. Stop that!*)

"Huh?" (My conversational skills were, as always, exceptional.)

"You one of the new students?" Confidently he punched the correct combination and the door clicked open.

"Yeah." We entered the utility room.

"When do you get off?"

"Huh?"

"When. Do. You. Get. Off."

"Uh, uh, uh…in a few minutes. Why?"

"Want to have a drink?"

(*A drink. Oh, yes. And a long, sweaty, dark, groping, grasping, gasping, panting, uh, uh, uh…. roll in the hay, yessir.*)

"Uh, what?"

"Do. You. Want. To. Have. A. Drink?"

"A drink?"

"A beverage. Wet coldness in a glass. Alcohol. With. Me. Do. You. Want. To. Have. A. Drink. With. Me?"

" Sure."

"Meet me here at six-fifteen. In front of this door. Can you do that? Can you remember that?"

"Sure."

"What is your name?"

"Huh?"

"What is your name?"

"Sarah."

"Sarah, my name is Steven."

And that was that.

Just Like Cherry Ames

The same night that I unclogged Mrs. G's drain, Steven and I and Moe went to a party in one of the residents' apartment blocks near the hospital. Steven had taken me around the corner for our first date, a beer at The West Side Brewery, and after three more beers, I had called Moe to invite her to the party.

"There's going to be *men* there," I implored her answering machine. That would be all it took to lure her. Cro-Magnon Man be damned!

Moe had a way of dressing that no one could emulate. She still bought her clothes at used-clothing places, the Salvation Army and Goodwill, as she had done in California, yet she always looked as though she had just invented the latest look. That night, she was working on a sort of punk-cum-biker-chick look—leather pants, tons of silver bracelets, a torn-up sweatshirt with the sleeves cut off, impossibly large triple-stranded blue beads.

She had brushed her naturally blond, naturally curly hair casually up into a sort of loose bun with the little "fuck-me tendrils," as we called them, cascading down her neck.

"Is that your friend?" Steven asked as Moe approached. "She *is* hot."

Steven and I were hanging out in a corner on a dusty sofa, half making out, half conversing, when Moe came over.

"Where's the bar?" she asked Steven, then, as an afterthought, "You must be— "

"Steven."

"You must be Steven. I must be Maureen."

Steven jumped up.

"What can I get you?"

Men immediately surrounded Moe as she made her way to the makeshift bar with Steven. That was the story of my life—always best friends with the better-looking chick, always sitting and watching while the other was pawed and flirted with. Oh, well. I had my own boyfriend now. Maybe.

"She is *so* hot. Move over." Steven pushed his way back onto the sofa and played with my hair.

"Yeah, you've mentioned that," I said.

"Jealous?"

"Ahhh... fuck off."

"Do you eat with that mouth?" He planted his lips on me and inserted his tongue.

I wanted him so bad.

Of all the guys who surrounded Moe that night, she wound up with Rusty. He was a second-year psychiatry resident ("Think of it!" she rhapsodized. "Only on call *every ninth night!*"), he was tall and cute, and he had super-rich parents.

"Rusty!" Moe sighed the next day. We had terrible hangovers. Moe was making us lemon-lime Alka-Seltzers. "So WASPish. So all-American. So—*rusty.*"

"Just think of it. Soon we'll be getting our Mrs.M.D. degrees," she cackled. "Just like Cherry Ames!"

We clinked our fizzing glasses.

Moe actually meant Sue Barton, Student Nurse, whose books predated Cherry's by several decades. Cheerful, mischievous, fertile Sue was the star of such paperback potboilers as "Student Nurse," "Senior Nurse," "Visiting Nurse," "Rural Nurse," "Superintendent of Nurses" and "Staff Nurse." Cherry Ames, a perky, Titian-haired, buxom student nurse, although somewhat sexier than Sue, couldn't be ever so bothered with the scores of hunky, manly surgeons, interns and medical students she encountered daily. She was far too busy solving mysteries and saving lives. Plus, she was probably a lesbian.

Slut Barton, on the other hand, snagged her Mrs.M.D. degree *before she finished nursing school*, becoming engaged to Dr. Bill Barry at the end of "Sue Barton: Senior Nurse."

Moe had searched used bookstores all over Manhattan for Sue Barton and Cherry Ames books. When we grew tired of studying, she would read excerpts aloud to me, inserting pornographic passages as needed.

" *'He saw then, and caught his breath, lifting her hand to his cheek, to hold it there.'* "

" *' Very proper and demure,' he said. 'Tell me, Miss Barton – Sue – if I may call you that – ' He faltered; then, still with forced lightness— 'Dare I ask again for your hand in marriage?'* "

" *'Oh, Dr. Rusty! Is that a— a— reflex hammer in your pocket?'* "

"That's us!" Moe shouted, waving the tattered paperback at me.

" *'Oh, Rusty, yes, yes, yes! I* will *become Mrs. Dr. Rusty! Just as soon as I get out of San Quentin in three to seven years!* "

"Then you can be 'Sue Barton: Cellblock Nurse.' "

"And *you* can be 'Cherry Ames: Saloon Nurse.'"

"And then you can be 'Sue Barton: Nurse-Parolee.' "

"And then *you* can be 'Cherry Ames: Slut Extraordinare.' "

"And then *you* can be 'Sue Barton: Impaired Nurse.' "

"And then *you* can be 'Cherry Ames: Twelve-Step Nurse.' "

"*I'll* be solving mysteries and having sex with women *and* men. You'll be doing the twelve steps, raising four children and keeping house for Ol' Doc Rusty, a simple country psychiatrist."

Moe looked puzzled.

"Sue has four children?"

(She hadn't yet read "Sue Barton: Staff Nurse.")

"Oh, well. …. Oh, Rusty! Rusty, Rusty, Rusty! Yes, yes, yes, fill me with sperm! *Oh*, Rusty! You are *so* well endowed! Yes! Yes! Yes! *Yeeeessssssssssssss!"*

Moe paused, post-fake-orgasm, and turned to me, her face radiant. "Oh, Cherry! Let's have a double wedding ceremony! I'll wear my leather pants. You'll wear your nursing school uniform. Our grooms will wear little tiny shorts. We'll go on our honeymoons together! Think of it! Sue and Cherry team up at last! 'Sue Barton and Cherry Ames: Honeymoon Nurses!' "

"We'll get 'honeymoon cystitis!' "

"Honeymoon cystitis" was a common female ailment—a urinary tract infection caused by too-frequent sex with a new partner.]

" 'Sue and Cherry and the Case of Shipboard Syphilis.' "

"Okay, stop now."

" 'Sue and Cherry Cure a Ham.' "

"Okay, that's enough."

" 'Sue and Cherry Put Out for the Navy.'"

"Stop it!"

Steven

His name was Steven, he was a first-year surgery intern, and his every-other-night-on-call
schedule, for some reason, rendered him unbelievably horny. He hadn't had a girlfriend in more
than a year, he smelled great, and he liked me!

Sex with Steven was a life-changing experience. I hadn't had good sex in more than three
years, since Hank, my last serious boyfriend. In
the intervening period, my friend Rose had set me
up on one or two disastrous blind dates with assistant district attorneys and I'd had a few gropes
here and there as well as some drunken, low-self-
esteem-driven one- or two-night stands, but the
sex had been mediocre in all cases. I had all but
given up on good sex.

Not only did Steven really like sex, but he also
knew where all my parts were. Although he was
on an orthopedic surgical track, he was supreme-

ly knowledgeable regarding female reproductive anatomy.

He could arouse me insanely with just one surgically trained finger. In fact, he loved to discreetly slip his hand down my pants at the movies, concerts, lectures—almost any sit-down occasion, really. Once he fingered me at a dive-y restaurant on a Friday night, his hand slipping under the long table during a residents' night out.

These end-of-the-week drink-fests were legendary within the surgery program at NYCAS. Only junior residents went. Chiefs and attendings were not welcome. Nurses were only invited if they were currently doing a junior surgery resident. Whoever was not on call was supposed to attend. The residents brought girlfriends, wives and lovers, but we were expected to entertain ourselves—unless, that is, we relished watching large, hairy, loutish young men chugging beer, shouting hoarsely, mock-fighting, arguing, bicep-punching and interrupting each other, describing their latest cases and griping about their chief residents, the private surgery attendings and the operating-room nurses.

This was a social occasion where long, seemingly pointless stories ended abruptly with such knee-slapping *bon mots* as:

"…. And when we got in there we found a *Wilm's tumor*! Heh-heh-heh-heh! A freakin' *Wilm's tumor*! D'you b'lie'dat?", or:

"… Get the fuck oudda here! Whaddaya mean, a spiral fracture? That's *freakin' impossible*, dude!", or:

"… *full of cancer*. Just freakin' *riddled* – peritoneum, omentum, the whole nine yards. Just *shot through*."

("Why do you subject yourself to this shit?" Moe demanded. "Are you afraid he'll stop hanging out with you if you don't go?"

I couldn't explain it. I just liked being around him.)

I had drunk most of a pitcher of watery beer by myself. It was about nine o'clock. The room stank of rotting peanut shells, stale cigarette smoke, and flat beer. I was playing with the salt shaker and chatting with one of the girlfriends, a very young, very sincere, very enthusiastic, very blond nurse of the Young & Clueless variety.

Kelly (*of course*—Kelly) was a surgical nurse. She assumed—incorrectly—that I was interested in surgical nursing because I had met my boyfriend while on a surgical nursing rotation. She had a high, babyish voice and ended every sentence, even simple declarative ones, with an emphatic upturn, as though asking a question. To wit:

"I think it's just *terrible*? When the nurse is supposed to *undermedicate* the patient? He may be in terrible *pain*? But we only give him ten of *morphine*? I mean, I'm supposed to be a patient *advocate*?"

If I were in a comic strip, my thought-balloon would have read, "Do I look like I give a shit?," when I felt my pants being undone. Before I could object or get my hands under the table, Steven was stroking, stroking, stroking and I was getting wet, wet, wet.

The conversation became a little one-sided—thank God Kelly-girl was a talker—as I nodded and smiled and squirmed while he silently brought me to the Promised Land for a three-day weekend.

All with one finger.

He loved going down on me, which amazed me.

He did not, however, win the Angel Mama's Best Boy Award.

An ancient hazing ritual of the Hell's Angel's, Moe assured me, was that an Angel-to-be had to go down on a Hell's Angel girlfriend (an "Angel Mama") while she was menstruating. This was called "earning your red wings."

"Were you an Angel Mama?" I asked her admiringly. (After all, she was from California.)

"Naw," Moe said, "but my brother knew someone who was." We were eating lunch (lettuce, blue cheese dressing, olives, saltines, tap water—$2.45) in the NYCAS School of Medicine cafeteria.

For a man to go to the Y, to eat pussy, to kiss Kitty, while you were having your period – this was the *ultimate* in sexual worship.

I have not experienced it personally.

[Fast-forward: Many years later, Moe had a boyfriend who clearly wanted to be a Hell's Angel. She met him at a Chanukah party given by one of the Ob/Gyn attendings at our hospital. His name was Harold J. Davis, and he was the host's tenant, occupying the upper floors of the East Village brownstone owned by the attending physician.

Moe and Harold J. Davis had an instantaneous attraction. You could feel the energy between them. They were practically grooming each other, as higher primates do while courting.

For about a seven-week period after the party, Moe was a fuck-goddess. Harold J. Davis, a real estate attorney, had an insatiable appetite, and he lacked only a Harley, or he would have been in the Hell's Angels hall of fame for sure.

"I just can't believe it. Our wildest dreams have come true!" Moe's voice had a furry quality to it. It was almost irritating, she was so *relaxed*.

"Whoa, what do you mean, *'our* wildest dreams'? He didn't taste *my* tampon," I reminded her.

"Shhhhhh!"

We were in the "Pet Care" aisle of the Odd Job.

"Shhhhh *what*? You don't want anyone to know that he *devoured your decidua*? *"

"Stop it!" Moe turned to me, mock-angry, and shoved a bag of dry cat food into my stomach.

"But shouldn't we tell the world that he *munched your menses*?"

"I *mean it now!*"

"You're ashamed of the fact that hat he *chewed your compacta? Sampled your spongiosa? Enjoyed your endometrium?**"*

"Stop it!" She hissed. "We won't be *welcome here any more* if you don't *stop right now!*"

A couple of nights after Harold J. Davis' Hell's Angel hazing, Moe and I were plenty surprised when her answering machine, flashing one message, played back the following:

"Hello, Maureen. This is *Harold J. Davis*. Call me."

Isn't that a little *formal* for someone who has gone down on you while you're having your period?

Can we all agree on this? Anyone who has ingested your monthly waste has earned the right to say, "Yo, it's me."]

* *Decidua is one medical name for the disposable uterine lining that is shed every 28 days, on average, as menstrual blood. See "deciduous."*

** *Compacta and spongiosa are the upper layers of the endometrium, the mucous membrane that lines the uterus.*

Back to the present: Steven was a very good lover, and he restored—nay, reinvented—my interest in sex. Perhaps most amazing of all, he who was on call every other night, he who worked twenty-six hours at a time, who should have cherished his sleep as one values his own life, liked to wake me up in the middle of his every-other-night off-call with a nice firm erection against my butt-crack. In other words, Steven wanted to have sex with me more than Steven wanted to sleep. Imagine that! When I was with Steven, he made me feel that we had all the time in the world.

It is midnight. I am trying to extract myself from Steven's bed to go home. There's almost no point, as I have "clinical" at 7 a.m., way uptown, and will not make it back to the West Village until 1 a.m. at the earliest, shower and go to bed, only to get up again in three and a half hours. But I have no extra clothes with me, I am dirty, I smell like sex, and I need to feed the cats.

"Stay," Steven moans, grabbing my arm. He has been doing this same routine for the past fifteen minutes.

"I gotta go! Get off me!"

"Five more minutes." He cups my breast with his big paw. "I'll make it worth your while..."

"Steven. *Do you understand*? I am trying to graduate from this shit-hole of a nursing school so that I can go to midwifery school. Can you please respect that?"

"Why do you need to go to school to be a midwife? It's just playing catch! I'll buy you a catcher's mitt and you can sterilize it!"

"Are you being disrespectful of my chosen profession?"

"Awww, don't get all sensitive." He is stroking the small of my back in little, frantic circles as I pull on my socks.

"Then why can't you respect my need to get home and get ready for my clinical tomor- —today?"

"All right, just go. But look what you're missing!" He yanks the covers back to reveal a massive erection, straining to escape the confines of his briefs.

Moe's words echo in my ears as I pull on my shirt:

"Never say no to a good erection. It might be your last."

"Awwww, Steven… Jeez…. I gotta go!" I yank my pants up, throw my jacket over my shoulder and open the door.

"Call me."

"See you."

Oh well. A good erection can always be recreated.

I'll tell that one to Moe next time I talk to her. She can add it to her repertoire.

Vicious Hungry Elevator Whores Get Screwed Automatically

It was Friday night. Lydia, Moe, Peter, Peter's boyfriend Mel and I were at Chez Moe, studying for our "Deviations from Health" midterm on Monday. Have I already mentioned this? In nursing, there is no disease, just an *alteration in the normal*, a *deviation from health*, if you will. This same course would be called "Pathophysiology" in medical school, because we were studying the diseases that affect major organ systems. But no! The massive heart attack that has rendered you a slab of meat in the I.C.U. is merely a *deviation from health*, Mr. Jones. That cancer that's devouring your pancreas? Don't fret, Ms. Smith. That's just an *alteration in metabolism related to disease process*.

We five were the masters of mnemonics. Mnemonics are great for short-term memorization: You could ace a nursing exam almost entirely on mnemonics; five years later, you could have a gun pointed at your head and would still not be able to recall what SHMOBRGR once stood for. Our goal was to winnow down gigantic concepts to the teeniest possible syllables for easy digestion and rapid regurgitation.

"Okay, who's got one for atherosclerosis?" Moe queried. We glanced quickly at our textbooks. Sometimes we gave impromptu awards to the person who came up with the niftiest memorization devices. I had already won a plush talking dog, a pink plastic tampon holder and a Snoopy-head pencil.

"Atherosclerosis," Peter intoned. "Causative factors: Cholesterol, Diet, Inheritance and Hemodynamics. CHID?"

"**C**hildren **I**nherit **H**eart **D**isease!" Lydia called out triumphantly.

"Everybody got it? Cholesterol, Inheritance, Hemodynamics and Diet! Children—causative factors." Moe was ecstatic. "Damn nice, Lydia!"

"Okay, guys," she continued, "complications of atherosclerosis? Obstruction of blood flow, formation of thrombi, and movement of thrombi to other areas. Anyone?"

I racked my brain: **o**bstruction, **t**hrombus formation, **m**igration. … skinny vessels, thrombi, **e**mboli … S… T…E…... E.S.T. … electroshock therapy.…

"How about, the children who inherit heart disease are named **O**tis, **T**imothy and **M**atthew?"

Peter suggested. "Obstruction, thrombi, movement."

"I've got it!" I shouted. "The kids are called Timothy, Otis, and Emily. E for embolus!"

"Perfect!"

Lydia dutifully copied our brilliant reductions onto five identical flash cards and passed them to everyone.

"Now, the risk factors for atherosclerosis," Moe said, moving along. "Age, Sex, Behavior, Hypertension, Cigarettes, High cholesterol. That's going to be hard."

"**C**ool **A**ging **H**yper **B**ehaviorists **S**moke after **S**ex," Mel suggested. "*Cool*-esterol—get it?"

Sometimes the mnemonics degenerated. It was hard to concentrate during an exam, for example, when the question, "clinical manifestations of renal disease include... " brought to mind "**U**nfortunate **A**ssholes **P**ut **D**ildoes **E**verywhere. **H**ow **C**an **O**live **H**ave **P**ain?" (Uremia, Azotemia, Proteinuria, Diuresis, (renal) Edema, Hematuria, Cylindruria, Oliguria, Hyposthenuria, Pyuria).

Or the one for the theoretical etiology of diabetes mellitus, my personal fave:

Vicious **H**ungry **E**levator **W**hores **G**et **S**crewed **A**utomatically! (Viruses, Histocompatibily, Ethnicity, Weight, Genetics, Socioeconomic {factors}, Autoimmune {disease}).

Or how about the one for the metabolic functions of the liver:

Sundays, **S**ome **S**luts **M**ay **C**ome (Secretory, Synthetic, Storage, Metabolic, Circulatory).

We were irreverent, but we studied hard. Yes, we consumed alcohol while studying, but in general, we valued our study time, and we were determined to get the top grades in our class. After all, we were the outcasts: the oldies, the fags, the singles.

My GPA was 3.75; Moe's was 3.8, Peter's was 3.69, Mel's 3.75 and Lydia— Lydia was our valedictorian, with a GPA of 4.0. To this day, I can still remember what Vicious Hungry Elevator Whores stands for.

F.I.N.A.

This is the Demerol. This is the Demerol locked in the box. This is the Demerol locked in the box in the nurses' station at the medical center. This is the nurse who holds the keys to unlock the Demerol locked in the box in the nurses' station at the medical center. This is the anesthesiologist who takes the Demerol from the nurse who holds the keys to unlock the Demerol locked in the box in the nurses' station at the medical center.

This is the patient, all tattered and torn, waiting for the anesthesiologist to give him the Demerol locked in the box in the nurses' station at the medical center.

Throughout nursing school, we kept being warned of the possibility of becoming "impaired nurses." Visions of Sue Barton in a wheelchair, bravely caring for patients despite a missing arm, terrible scars, etc. Right?

Wrong. They meant *drug*-impaired nurses. Almost daily our instructors quoted the grim statistics about "impaired health-care professionals."

47

Anesthesiologists are the best candidates, because they have the most frequent access to pharmaceutical-quality narcs, uppers, barbs and 'pams [narcotics, stimulants, barbiturates and benzodiazepines (the family of drugs that are variants of diazepam, or "Valium" ((Such a *nice* family!)))]. Nurses are second best, because they hold the keys to unlock the drugs that impair the anesthesiologists.

Over and over we were told horror stories and shown graphic educational videos of nurses found cold and lifeless in their apartments; nurses accidentally removing patients' breathing tubes while impaired; nurses awakening in pools of their own vomit, not knowing where they were ("Sounds like a normal Thursday morning to me," Moe whispered.).

They told us graphic tales of rehab centers that *only nurses* could attend. And this was all because nursing, and medicine, are *stressful*. Even the most unlikely among us could possibly fall victim to temptation in a moment of *stress*.

We decided to form a campus organization, a secret society, if you will: The Future Impaired Nurses of America (F.I.N.A. – pronounced "FEYE-nah."). We had no access to keys or drugs, but alcohol was legal and plentiful.

The hazing ritual for F.I.N.A. was that you had to get so drunk that you vomited in a public place.

I chose the IRT No. 1 subway train, heading home late one night after a "study session." I was alone in the car, so it was an unwitnessed public puking (U.P.P.), but Moe and the others took my word for it. Plus, I was so hung over the next morning that I puked again, in the ladies' restroom outside the NYCAS Medical Center's Harry Stern Auditorium.

Moe was initiated in the presence of witnesses: me and our fellow sufferer Lydia who, like me, was a second-career person. (Officially, Moe was too, if you counted being a junkie as her first career.)

Moe chose to puke—or, rather, her puking reflex overwhelmed her (because, really, only bulimics *choose* to puke)—as we exited the subway station by the NYCAS Medical Center in Washington Heights.

Elegantly, tragically, she knelt by a little alcove just in front of the subway stairs leading up to Broadway.

A curious crowd—most on their way to work, some on their way to sell or buy drugs—gathered to watch. I swept Moe's hair back and Lydia held her book bag. I supplied Kleenex; Lydia murmured comforting words.

When Moe realized she had attracted an audience, she quickly recovered by saying as loudly as possible, "This baby is *killing* me!" The bystanders murmured, smiled sympathetically and dispersed.

Moe arose from her knees, newly perky.

"I'm starving! Do we have time for a bite before class?"

Lydia took longer to puke publicly; thus she remained a novitiate for a longer time. Months after Moe and I were old F.I.N.A. hands, already preparing seminars for future international chapters, she finally gave it up in a large fountain in the lobby of the Ritz-Carlton Hotel. Although Moe and I were not there to cheer her on, her parents were pretty surprised. They were in town on business and she had agreed to meet them for a very early breakfast before lecture on Monday morning.

We even had an anthem. It went like this:

Impaired! Impaired! We live to be impaired!
Clap if you believe in FINA, from New York City
to Carolina!
Impaired in church or in a dinah (diner),
Impaired, impaired, impaired!
(raise a glass)

We mostly drank beer while studying, with seasonal variations. In fall and winter, we heated fresh cider and added equal parts Haitian rum. Balmy spring days called for tropical drinks, or *"bebidas festivas,"* such as Shark Bites, Mai Tais or Pina Coladas. Having a blender and plenty of crushed ice on hand was a membership requirement of F.I.N.A.

More formal occasions—such as sitting around whining about nursing school—called for vodka. The New York chapter—Moe, myself, Lydia, Peter and Mel—started out small, but we had great hopes for it.

[Fast-forward: I told my friend Philip about F.I.N.A. a couple of years later, when the novelty of getting trashed every night had long since worn off. By then Moe and I were well established as night nurses in Labor & Delivery at NYCAS—the Mecca—and we were far too exhausted to live up to F.I.N.A.'s rigid standards. We could barely manage drinks once a week.

Philip was a third-year anesthesiology resident, bright, cute, with a baby's face, a favorite among the L&D staff. Philip was always cheerful, always available, always concerned with the patients' wellbeing. Sometimes he would appear on the Labor floor in the middle of the night to check on patients who had had cesareans earlier. He was never crabby when paged, and always the first one there in an emergency. Everyone loved Philip. He was devoted to relieving pain.

Before every c-section, Philip always asked the charge nurse for 100 milligrams of Demerol. Most anesthesiology residents and attendings took 75 mgs of Demerol, but Philip always asked for 100. You could tell, in fact, when Philip was rotating through L&D, because the 100 mg. Demerol box, which usually sat unopened for weeks at a time, was always near empty.

One time I asked him why.

"Women who are having a cesarean under epidural or spinal anesthesia often won't need much IV medication initially," Philip explained. "The epidural or spinal will usually hold them until the baby's out. But they experience a rebound pain when the uterus is being repaired. If you give them 50 IV immediately before delivery of the uterus and then 25 shortly before they put it back in, they get complete relaxation. Then you give them the remaining 25 as the surgeons are closing the incision, and it has an additive effect to the regional anesthesia—sometimes they are comfortable for hours after the epidural or spinal has worn off."

"But what about really skinny women? Don't they need less?"

Philip shook his head. "The woman's weight has less to do with it when it's major surgery. You might use less in labor when a woman's really skinny. But when they're on the table, opened up, they all have similar needs for narcotic analgesia."

Made sense to me.

The NYCAS annual Ob/Gyn Christmas party was a festive event. Imagine all the people you couldn't stand to be around all year, made softer and fuzzier by alcohol and cocktail franks, dressed in bad formal wear and shiny rented tuxes, with bad hair and big puffy bangs, dancing clumsily under a disco ball in the auditorium. So tragic that Christmas comes but once a year!

Moe and I sat in a corner waiting for our dates. I was still with Steven. Miraculously, our relationship—which was based almost entirely on sex, esp. oral—had survived nursing school, my nursing boards and my nightmarish hazing at NYCAS. Steven was now a senior resident in Orthopedics at St. Elizabeth's Medical Center in Newark, and we had developed a grudging sort of fondness for one another after so much time.

It was going to be over soon, though. I wanted—well, I wanted what everybody else wanted—to be married and own real estate and have children, but probably not with Steven.

Which was convenient, because Steven, who was five years younger than I, wanted to drive a Porsche, do arthroscopic surgeries, brag about it over pitchers of beer with his hairy pals, and date lots of women.

I had considered breaking up with Steven many times.

"Are you crazy?" Moe asked. "You'd give up occasional, familiar, good sex in exchange for *no sex at all*?"

Moe was dating a one-fourth-Ethiopian, one-fourth Nigerian, half-Jewish (Steven would argue that you cannot possibly be *half*-Jewish) resident in internal medicine named Oberon Selassie Oboyegene. We called him Oso.

Oso had developed the curious habit of shouting Maureen's full name, along with that of Jesus Christ, as he was coming. I had never personally witnessed it, but depending on her mood, Moe was sometimes willing to do an impersonation:

"Oh, oh, oh, *Jesus!* Oh, Maureen
Conaway!" *Oh* Jesus!
Oh, my love! Oh, Maureen
Conaway! Oh *Jesus!* Oh,
my love! Oh, oh, oh, OOOOOOOOHHHHH
Maureen Conaway! My love! *Oh Jesus!"*

Moe was wearing a shimmery black cocktail dress that she had picked up at a used-clothing store for $14. I was wearing a midnight-blue minor-designer evening gown that I had purchased years before during my journalist phase. We were both bitching about the control-top pantyhose that gave us wedgies in the front—vaginal wedgies, if you will. Moe called them "Nazi pantyhose."

I spied Oso entering the auditorium, looking around nervously for Maureen Conaway.

"Oh, oh, oh, *Jesus!* Oh, Maureen Conaway! *OH MY GOD!* There he is!" I pointed out Oso in the crowd, steadily approaching us.

"Shhhhhhh! What are you doing? He'll hear you!"

"Good evening, Maureen and Sarah. You look lovely." He pretended to bow low.

"Thank you, Oso. You look very hot yourself."

"Where is Steven?"

"Steven is late, as is often the case."

"Do you want to dance?" He pulled Moe up by the hand. The band was playing a Donna Summer song and the big-bangers and shiny tuxes were doing their pitiful best on the makeshift dance floor.

"Have you heard from Philip?" Moe asked me before Oso whirled her away. They were gone before I could answer.

Philip had promised to come to the party as our guest. I wondered what Steven would think of him. I talked about Philip often, and Steven actually expressed jealousy once in a while.

("Why don't you go out with him if he's so great and perfect?" Steven had barked at me once when I was rhapsodizing about Philip. "Why do you waste your time with me?" I had had to flatter and compliment Steven for almost an hour after that to appease his hurt, little-boy-surgeon feelings.)

My friend Cheryl, an Ob/Gyn resident, strolled by.

"Hey, Sarah. Where's Moe? Where's Philip? Where's Steven?"

"Dancing with Oso; haven't seen him; late."

"I'm going to overhead-page him."

A few minutes later, during a band break, I heard the electronic voice of Patti Page, the ubiquitous computerized overhead operator:

"Dr. Philip Parker. Paging Dr. Philip Parker. Please report to the main auditorium. Dr. Parker to the main auditorium."

"Look who we found." Moe and Oso appeared, with Steven trailing behind.

"It's about time. Late case?"

Steven kissed my ear. He was so full of himself that year, what with getting to do major orthopedic cases and all. He loved telling me bone-crunching stories, describing crush injuries and diagramming ligament repairs for me. I was learning a lot about orthopedics, actually.

"Still no Phil?"

"Yeah. I don't know where he is. Cheryl Patti Paged him a while ago."

Three-thirty a.m. I was dreaming of white laboratory rats grown out of control, as big as cats, turned loose in the auditorium among the dancers. The phone rang.

"Uh-huh. Uh-huh. Yeah, she's here. Yeah, I'll put her on."

Steven handed me the phone and turned over.

"Sarah? It's Cheryl. I have some awful news. Philip is dead."

"No, that can't be right." I sat up and turned on the lamp. "He was supposed to come to the party."

"Sarah, he's dead. He OD'd. His roommate found him in their apartment. We worked on him for more than two hours in the E.R. They even cracked his chest. He's dead."

"No, that can't be. He was supposed to come to the party. *You overhead-paged him.* Was he dead when you overhead-paged him?"

"Sarah, I've got to go to sleep now. I'll call you in the morning. I'm sorry."

The E.R. code team was so hungry to save one of its own that they had opened Philip's chest with the bone saw and rib spreader, Cheryl told me afterwards. This was after they performed CPR, intubated him, ambu-bagged him and gave IV epinephrine, atropine, Narcan and lidocaine, and administered multiple shocks to his heart for more than two hours.

Dr. Richard Boylan, the chairman of the Department of Anesthesiology, a burly, red-haired 50-something man who hunted big game for sport, stood by the door of the trauma room and watched without speaking as the code team carried out its grim task. Occasionally, Cheryl said, he reached over and felt Philip's ankles, as though looking for a pulse.

Finally, after Philip's chest was wrenched open and the internal paddles were being applied over and over, Dr. Boylan pulled Cheryl aside.

"Make them stop," he said.

"I don't know if I can do that," Cheryl told him.

"His body is cold. Make them stop."

At the memorial for Philip, Dr. Boylan, whose only son had been killed in a bicycle accident at age 20, wept as he delivered the opening remarks. He spoke of Philip's dedication to his job, his energy, his love for his family, his compassion and his unique ability to comfort patients undergoing surgery.

"This is what they warned us about in nursing school," Moe whispered.

I sat next to Steven, who had no expression. Moe sat with Cheryl in the row ahead of me.

"What do you mean?"

"Don't you remember? They said that impaired health-care workers don't necessarily show signs. They said to watch out for the popular, energetic, good-natured ones who are always awake when you page them and who are always cheerful. That was Philip! We missed the signs!" Moe began to cry.

Philip had mainlined enough Sufentanil ("Sufenta") to kill an elephant, Cheryl told us. It didn't seem like a suicide, though; more like an accidental overdose. Fentanyl—a synthetic narcotic—is one hundred times stronger than morphine, and Sufentanil is ten times stronger than Fentanyl. Philip, who had been taking that extra Demerol for himself every time he did a c-section, was preparing for the party, perhaps. The amount he took was about four times what would be given to a patient during the course of a complicated all-day surgery such as a multiple organ transplant. The fact that he took so much of the drug was an indication, Cheryl said, of the probable depth and duration of his addiction.

Three days later I got a Christmas card in the mail.

"Dear Sarah, It was great working (and playing) with you in 1991. Looking forward to a wonderful 1992. Love, Philip."]

Moe

This is Moe:

I am sitting on the steps of the NYCAS Health Sciences Library. A pale, thin young woman with naturally blond hair in a loose French braid sits directly across from me on Step No. 5. It is the second week of nursing school.

A guy in scrubs walks by—no neck, hairy chest, hairy arms, with bulging delts and biceps. Kinda cute.

"Ortho," the young woman says quietly.

Is she talking to me?

"Are you talking to me?"

"Ortho."

"I beg your pardon?"

"I'm playing 'guess the specialty.' "

"Specialty?"

"Of the residents who walk by. The big hairy ones with the muscular arms are always Ortho."

"Really?" I move closer. She smells of jasmine.

"You know what they say about Orthopods. 'Strong as an ox, and twice as smart.' "

A Sikh walks by, eyes cast down at the sidewalk, lab coat slapping the breeze, the sun reflecting off his bright white turban.

"Medicine."

"Medicine?"

"Internal Medicine. Sikhs are never surgeons."

"How do you know so much?"

"I don't, really. I just like looking at men. There are so many men here." She pauses. "Aren't we in nursing school together?" She offers her hand. "Maureen Conaway. Call me Moe."

"Sarah Porter." I am ashamed that I don't recognize her.

"I'm sorry—I haven't been able to— "

"Look anyone in the eye yet?"

"I'm a little—"

"Appalled?"

"Well, yeah. I mean, everyone's, like—*thirteen*."

"Tell me about it. I stayed in the dorm for a week until my apartment was ready. These girls are out of control! Running down the halls in their flannel nightgowns and bunny slippers, popping popcorn day in and day out, screaming. I could probably sue the school for brain damage."

"Where do you live now?"

"The East Village."

"You're kidding! I live in the West Village."

"Wow, cool. What are you doing after class?"

"Nothing."
"Wanna get trashed?"

Or this is Moe:
"Shut up."
We are walking in silence down University Place towards my apartment at dusk.
"But I didn't say anything!"
"But you were *about to*."

Or this is Moe:
We have just left a free concert in Central Park. We are quite drunk. It is a balmy summer evening, and we have no classes tomorrow.
"*Look at that hunk*. Yo, officer!"
The mounted cop is startled. He sees Moe— who can resist her? —and trots his horse over to us. He is young and hunky.
"Give us a ride!"
"I can't, Miss. I'm on duty. I'll get in trouble. I'll take your number, though."
"Give me a ride and I'll give you my number."
The officer, shaking in fear, helps Maureen up to the front of his saddle.
"You can't tell anyone about this," he pleads.
"Giddyup!"
They trot away down the path, deeper into the park. I wait. A few minutes later, they return, the officer pale and sweaty, Maureen giggling. She lets herself down from the big horse's back, holding the officer's hand for a second longer than

she has to after dismounting. Using his pen, she writes her phone number on his palm.

"Call me!" she shouts as we walk away.

Or this is Moe:

I am late for "Deviations from Health" class. I peer through the window of the classroom door. There, in the last row, twirling a strand of hair around her fingers, is someone who looks like Moe, only—she has purple hair.

I slide into the seat next to her. The teacher is droning on about renal failure.

"What the fuck happened to your hair?"

"What do you mean?"

"It's purple!"

"It's supposed to be 'blue-black.' That's what the box said."

"Why did you dye your hair?"

"I don't know. I felt like it. Don't you like it?"

"No, I do not like it. Can you fix it? Can it be reversed?"

Just then the instructor asked pointedly, "Sarah, do you have something to share with the rest of the class?"

Or this is Moe:

We are talking about anal intercourse. It is, Moe says, "What all men want. And all women fear."

For some reason, it is a recent obsession of ours. Maybe it was our newfound future profession, midwifery, where sex was the beginning of everything; maybe it was our current drudgery, so tied up with shit.

"You know," I say, "a medium-size penis is about the same caliber as a well-formed stool."

Moe considers this for a moment, then responds, "Yeah, but the stool isn't saying, '*I'm going in! I'm coming out! I'm going in! I'm coming out!*'"

Or this is Moe:

"I was a junkie in Oakland."

"What?"

"You asked what I used to do in California. I was a junkie."

"You mean, like, a heroin addict?"

"Yep. I lived with my boyfriend Ralphie, I waited tables, and I was a heroin addict. Kind of."

"How did you—how long did you— "

"Stay a heroin addict? Not long. About eight months. Before that I did it off and on for a few years, but I wasn't an addict. Ralphie was really getting seriously addicted. It was a problem. He stole things and shit. So I split. There were free clinics in Oakland, so I checked into one. I got clean pretty quick. It wasn't that bad. Then I flew out here, and lived with my Mom for a year, getting my shit together. I decided I wanted to be a midwife. Then, the next thing you know, I was in nursing school, having my personality surgically removed."

[Fast-forward: My phone rings at 4:45 a.m. Moe and I have been staff nurses at NYCAS for almost a year.

"Josh is dead."

Josh is Moe's younger brother. Josh is 24 years old.

"Moe? What are you saying?"

"Come to Josh's apartment. I need you."

Moe's younger brother, Joshua, had moved to New York from Connecticut to be near his sister when she started nursing school. He was six years younger, her only sibling, and they were deeply attached to each other. Josh had had major depression for most of his adolescence, twice trying to commit suicide while still in high school.

He was on a million meds, which he forgot to take sometimes. Once Moe got called by the police when Josh "slipped" onto the subway tracks and was admitted to the short-stay psychiatric unit at Bellevue Hospital. Another time he was arrested for shoplifting a leather jacket and Moe had to get her mother to wire cash to a Western Union office, and go downtown to Central Booking to bail him out.

He had an apartment in Washington Heights, near the hospital. His mother paid the rent. He didn't work —"not yet," Moe said. He was "working on getting himself together."

Josh was gorgeous—Irish-looking, with deep blue eyes and rusty, not quite red hair. He was brilliant, and funny, and sarcastic and charismatic and tragic, and we loved being around him. We used to joke about all of us living together. I fantasized that Josh would fall in love with me—I was convinced that my love could lift him out of his depression and make him stop drinking and taking drugs and passing out in strange places.

The outer door to Josh's building was hanging open, and someone had actually taped the inner door so that it wouldn't lock. It was still dark out. It was early November.

The stairs had no light, and the carpeting smelled like mildew and urine. The door to his apartment was unlocked.

Moe was sitting on Josh's twin bed, leaning against the wall. She was holding Josh's head in her lap and reading "The Cat in the Hat."

I felt a wave of nausea.

"Moe, what's going on?" I stood in the doorway, afraid to come any closer.

"Look at me. Look at me. Look at me now! It is fun to have fun, but you have to know how."

"Maureen. What is going on?"

"It's Dr. Seuss. He loves Dr. Seuss. When he was a baby I used to read it to him all the time."

"Is he all right?"

I could tell before I got to the bed that Josh was not all right. His face was blue, his skin waxy. He was not breathing. I felt a sour taste in my mouth, the way you do just before vomiting.

"Moe, is he dead?"

"I already told you he's dead."

"Did you call the police?"

"I just want to read to him for awhile first."

"Maureen, we have to call the police."

"Why?"

"Because maybe he was murdered. Because he's dead. We have to call them now."

"He wasn't murdered. He OD'd, see?" She held up an empty pill bottle.

Josh had told his mother once that he wanted his body cremated and his ashes scattered over the Atlantic Ocean. Two weeks after Josh died, Moe and Moe's mother and I took the New Jersey Transit train to Sea Girt, New Jersey, where Moe's mother used to date a guy who owned a seafood restaurant. He had a small motorboat and had agreed to take us out a little ways from shore. There was a wet and icy wind. Moe's mother's headscarf blew off.

In the boat, holding my coat together at the neck to keep out the wind, I displayed photos of Josh that I had taken at a Fourth of July picnic at Moe's mother's house the summer before. I clutched them tightly by their corners as the wind slapped them ferociously.

We each told a story about Josh. Moe's mother told about his birth—how she had failed to notice that she was in labor because she was frantically crocheting a blanket for his crib, and how she almost delivered in the taxi.

Moe told a story about Josh as a little boy, how he was so tenderhearted he could not watch "Lassie" reruns without crying. Moe used to tease him by humming the "Lassie" theme song, and his eyes would well up and he'd yell, "*Stop it* now! I mean it!," and Moe would hold up her arm like an injured collie paw and make sad-collie eyes.

I had only known Josh for a couple of years. I didn't have too many endearing stories, since I'd mostly seen him drunk, or in trouble, or high. I told about Josh at the picnic the year before—how he'd entertained the next-door neighbor's two-year-old for hours by wearing a headband with devil horns and chasing the kid around the yard.

Moe read a poem by Emily Dickinson.

Ample make this Bed –
Make this Bed with Awe –
In it wait till Judgment break
Excellent and Fair.

Be its Mattress straight –
Be its Pillow round –
Let no Sunrise' yellow noise
Interrupt this Ground—

"Well, that's pretty grim, Maureen," Moe's mother said.

"Ma, he liked the grim stuff."

We each took a handful of ashes and threw them unceremoniously into the raw air. They fell upon the slate-gray water and floated for a while before they were washed away. The sun came out for one brief moment just then, dappling the flat gray surface with Day-Glo orange before disappearing behind cloud cover again.

The Death of the Ball-Turret Gunner

During the long and torturous days of nursing school, it was hard for me to remember why I had left a world where people returned your phone calls within six minutes for a world where excreted body fluids were tallied in cubic centimeters at the end of every eight hours.

In journalism, words were revered, massaged for greater meaning, lovingly tweaked and paired with other, equally beautiful words to seduce the reader and lay the scene. In nursing school, language was butchered brutally all day long. In nursing school, I learned a new "word that can't be verbed"—such as *parent, liaison, dialogue, outreach, pressure, impact, reference*—almost every day.

In journalism, stories that were pointless, dated or irrelevant didn't make it into the paper. In nursing school, the most meaningless topics imaginable were fodder for three-hour lectures.

In journalism, clichés were eschewed. In nursing school, children were repeatedly referred to as "little people," while big people carried on enthusiastic discussions about bed linens and suction catheters and the benefits of finger cots—little rubber condoms worn over individual fingers—versus gloves for manually removing the impacted feces from someone's rectum.

Whereas journalists tended to have a sense of humor, were literate and sarcastic and made irreverent jokes, people in nursing—at least at the leadership levels—were about as funny as a bowel prep before surgery. Plus they took themselves far too seriously.

If it hadn't been for Moe, Lydia, Steven, Rose and a few other friends from my past life, my brain would have turned into rice pudding.

Despite the steady diet of pablum I was fed in the didactic portion of my nursing education, however, in the clinical part something amazing began to happen. Being in a position of utter vulnerability, doing something every day that I'd never done before, at high risk of doing it incorrectly, unattractively or clumsily somehow made me, instead of really bitchy, *open* to experience in a way I couldn't remember ever having been before.

Taking care of vulnerable people, even—perhaps especially—when I had no idea what I was doing, and being vulnerable myself, made it possible for me to see things differently, less globally, more narrowly, with a focus on the day to day, like living on a small farm in a harsh climate.

My epiphany came one morning in late winter. I awoke before the alarm and sat up in the dark. I could hear the songs of house finches piercing the absolute stillness of West Eleventh Street at 5 a.m. One would sing out, there'd be a terrifying pause—complete silence—and then another would pick up the tune, altering it slightly.

How long since I noticed this?

I was filled with loathing and dread for the day that stretched before me. That day I was to care for a stroke victim who apparently lacked all cognitive function. Her joints had stiffened to the point of deformity, and most of the day would consist of flushing her various IV lines, changing catheters, trying to extend her contracted elbows and wrists, and bathing her.

Her room (we were required to visit the patient the evening before our "experience" and review the chart)—stank of old, concentrated urine. It was blinding.

There was to be no redeeming value in caring for this patient.

I was not fully awake yet, but already I was nauseated.

"Oh, well. Maybe she coded."

Had I just said those words aloud?

Had I just wished someone dead so that I would not have to suffer the inconvenience of caring for her?

What was happening to me? Was I not human any more? *I was going to be a midwife. I was going to bring babies into the world. I was going to do something important. I was going to help people.*

That day, as I bathed Mrs. S and changed her lines and tubes, I recited every bit of poetry I had ever memorized. My father, who had become a professor of comparative literature in the middle of his life after years as a successful businessman, had encouraged me to memorize poetry every day when I was growing up, and I was glad for it now.

Unashamed, I recited continuously, and with a powerful resonance.

"Do you like Dylan Thomas? How about this one?" I recited "A Refusal to Mourn the Death, By Fire, of a Child in London." I did the last line the way I had heard Dylan Thomas himself do it, on a scratchy old recording my dad used to play for me, with a query built into the last word; not a bald, declarative statement, but a possible question:

After the first death, there is no other (?).

I rubbed her elbow vigorously between my hands to warm the joint, then began stretching it.

"Is this okay? Is this good?"

"What about Robert Frost? This is one of my favorites:"

Some say the world will end in fire,
Some say in ice.
From what I've tasted of desire,
I hold with those who favor fire.
But if it had to perish twice,
I think I know enough of hate
I'd say that for destruction ice
Is also great
and would suffice.

As I changed her bed with her in it, I recited Theodore Roethke's "The Sloth":

In moving-slow he has no Peer.
You ask him something in his ear;
He thinks about it for a Year;

And then, before he says a Word,
There, upside down (unlike a Bird)
He will assume *that you have Heard—*

"What are you doing?"

Phyllis, the actual nurse assigned to Mrs. S., stood in the doorway.

"I'm reciting poetry."

"She can't hear you."

"How do you know? Maybe she likes it."

Whether I tortured Mrs. S. with my poetic recall or whether she had a better day with me than her usual, I don't know. But I realized that I didn't have to dread taking care of people in enormously stressful circumstances. All I had to do was find a way to make them feel better for eight hours at a time.

It was a no-lose situation.

(Unless there was a trache involved.)

Charles H. was a handsome black man in his 40s. He was classified as a "T-12." Because of a gunshot wound to the lower abdomen, his spinal cord had been severed at the level of the 12th thoracic vertebra, near the bottom of the ribcage just at the start of the gentle concavity of the lumbar spine.

Charles had suffered spinal shock—a rare condition requiring life support until basic reflexes return—and had undergone extensive surgery to repair the damage to his internal organs, but his spinal cord could not be fixed. Now in his fourth week in the hospital, he was preparing to be transferred to a long-term rehabilitation facility. He was training himself, with the help of laxatives and stool softeners, to have a bowel movement at the same time each day. He would never voluntarily pee again. Sexual sensation was out of the question. And, of course, he would never walk, or run, or stand.

Charles had done two tours of duty in Vietnam. During a bombing raid in Danang, his left arm and chest were burnt so badly the damaged flesh now resembled ocean waves in a stop-action photograph. He had spent six months in an Army hospital in Virginia. After multiple skin grafts and rehabbing for almost a year, Charles had returned to New York, gone to college on the G.I. Bill, and had taken over his elderly father's business, a full-service gasoline station near Yankee Stadium.

For almost twenty years, Charles had endured robberies, break-ins, and gang fights, but he stayed in business. Over time, young boys from the projects started hanging out at his gas station, helping him with chores, telling him stories, seeking guidance.

One of the more troubled boys Charles knew, a 12-year-old named Jamal, had come to the station one evening to visit Charles and pick up a spiral ham that Charles had won in a raffle and promised to Jamal's mother. Jamal brought an older friend with him. The friend had a gun; he and Jamal got into an argument. In the struggle for control of the gun, Charles was shot in the belly.

Charles told me all of this as I was bathing him and changing his foley catheter on a dark, cold, rainy day in late April. Because he had no bladder control, he urinated by means of an "indwelling," or *foley catheter*—a soft rubber tube that is pushed through the *urethra* into the bladder and held in place by a little balloon filled with water. To avoid infection, the catheter had to be changed frequently.

Charles was not my first male patient, but it was my first time handling a penis for business rather than pleasure. I recalled Moe's advice about placing a foley catheter in a male patient, which she had taken verbatim from the surgical resident observing her:

"It's easier than a female. There's only *one hole.* Grab it like you love it and pull it to the ceiling!"

"Your first time?" Charles guessed as I fidgeted with the sterile glove pack.

"Oh, no." I wasn't sure what he meant, but it seemed better to pretend to be vastly experienced and confident.

Charles was so lacking in self-pity that he made it all right for me to do the kinds of things only a loved one should have to do for another. He seemed to have accepted his grim lot and was trying to get on with the business of being a person who cannot walk, stand, pee or experience physical pleasure. There was no bitterness that I could see.

We had just completed a nursing seminar on death and dying.

"Have you heard of Elisabeth Kübler-Ross? She's a psychiatrist who— "

"—wrote *On Death and Dying,* right?"

"Yeah, how did you—" I caught myself.

"You think an old, burnt-up Vietnam vet like me doesn't know about Elisabeth Kübler-Ross? I went to Hunter College on the G.I bill, Sarah. I was an English major just like you." He rubbed his thighs thoughtfully.

So where was Charles's denial, anger, bargaining?

"Oh, I already went through that," he said cheerfully.

"How do you do it, Charles?" I asked. "How can you be so—okay about all of this?"

I was massaging the withering muscles of his calves and rubbing his feet with a damp, scratchy washcloth. He couldn't feel it, but said it made him feel better anyway.

"I guess I had a good childhood," Charles said. "I can remember my mother telling me before I went to bed at night, 'I will always love you. I will always be with you. Nothing bad is going to happen to you.' I can't imagine how these kids that hang around my station get by these days. Do their parents ever tell them that they'll be okay, or that they are loved?"

He smoothed the sheets where he lay.

"Nothing bad has happened to me, Sarah," he said.

While Charles was getting dressed, we talked about my career path— from English major-journalist to nursing student-midwife—and he discussed his.

"I always wanted to be a vet," he said. "Not a Vietnam vet, but a veterinarian. Don't know how I ended up being a gas-station owner."

He paused and sighed. "My nephew is running the station until I finish rehab. I hope he can handle it."

I maneuvered his trousers over his feet and up to where his hands lay at his sides. He reached down and pulled them up. Then I helped him to a sitting position and gave him a clean pajama top to put on. It was growing dark. It was almost dinnertime.

Charles had never married and had no children.

Charles's senior English thesis at Hunter College, long ago, was on the poetry of war.

I balanced him on the edge of the bed—he showed me how to do it—and brought the wheelchair over, placing it at an angle to the bed and locking the wheels. He grasped the far side of it with his right hand and braced his left side against me.

"Some of my Vietnam buddies were here last night visiting me, and we were telling war stories," he said. "I woke up with a war poem in my head by James Dickey –– I think it was James Dickey."

I put my hands under his armpits. One, two, three—he swung himself into the wheelchair. His limp feet, on which he balanced lightly, bumped my legs. I felt the answer to his question before my mind formed the thought. This happens to me sometimes.

"Do you mean 'The Death of the Ball-Turret Gunner'? It's by Randall Jarrell."

"That's the one!" Charles exclaimed. "Don't know what made me say James Dickey."

"Do you remember the whole thing?" he asked excitedly. "It's short as hell. Can you recite it?"

I remembered it was very short; perhaps four or five lines, but I had never tried to memorize it. I shook my head.

Charles brightened. "Can you call me and read it to me when you get home tonight?"

At 9:45 p.m., I dialed Charles's room.

"From my mother's sleep I fell into the State,
And I hunched in its belly till my wet fur froze.
Six miles from earth, loosed from its dream of life,
I woke to black flak and the nightmare fighters.
When I died they washed me out of the turret with
a hose."*

"That's the one! What on earth do you think he meant by it?"

"I don't know, Charles. What does it mean, to 'fall into the State'?"

"It's a mystery, sweetie. A lot of war poems don't make much sense. But it's a vivid image, isn't it, that last line?"

"You get some rest, Charles."

"Thanks a lot, Sarah. You have a good life."

"Can I visit you, Charles, at the rehab place?"

"Sure you can—you know where it is. But you won't, honey. Soon you'll be graduating. You just get on with your life."

I never saw him again.

Part Two

Crying in the Bathroom

As a "graduate nurse," you are routinely sub-jected to the most egregious kinds of humiliation day after day. It's called *being a new nurse*. Because you do not know what you are doing, and because you are new at it, the simplest of tasks are seem-ingly insurmountable.

Out of financial necessity, and because most midwifery education programs preferred can-didates with Labor & Delivery experience, after graduation, Moe and I had immediately started working as staff nurses in Labor & Delivery at NYCAS. We had been warned that it would be a rough initiation. NYCAS was known for its high-risk obstetric patients, its multiple emergencies, its hard-as-nails nursing staff.

On the first day of orientation in Labor & Delivery, all new nurses participate in a "scaven-ger hunt." You are given a list of things, *viz.:*

Infant ambu bag (for resuscitating a newborn)

Pediatric suction tubing 8 fr, 10 fr, 12 fr (for suctioning snot from an infant)

Foley catheter and urine collection bag

Straight catheter kit (to remove urine from bladder)

Pediatric endotracheal tubes (for newborn resuscitation)

Adult ambu bag (for resuscitating an adult)

Adult suction tubing (big-time snot-suctioning, like a trache)

Razors (for shaving pubes prior to a cesarean section)

Angiocaths 18 gau., 16 gau., 14 gau. (for IV starting)

Pink tape (to secure IV)

IV tubing

IV tubing for controlled-infusion pump

IV "piggyback" setup (for giving meds into IV)

Pitocin (to make the uterus contract, to induce labor)

Methergine (to make the uterus contract, to control hemorrhage)

Oxygen mask

Oxygen tubing …

… and so on, and you and your orientation buddies, who may or may not be as lame as you, are given a time limit to find all these things and bring them to your "preceptor," a senior staff nurse in charge of your orientation, who is comparing your performance to every other "orientee" she has ever precepted, and you're not looking too good.

Moe and I collided at one point on that first day, frantically ripping open the drawers of a metal cabinet near the O.R., spewing miscellaneous tubing behind us, searching for life-saving items as time ran out.

"Know where the razors are?" Moe panted as she pawed through the top drawer while I plumbed the bottom one. "I found a whole stash by the nurses' station. In a plastic bag in a little wooden cabinet with a drawer missing."

The sweaty, nauseating panic I felt during the "scavenger hunt" persisted. Nightly I dreamed I was sleeping in an overheated room surrounded by chirruping, thumping fetal monitors, and I woke up with my heart hammering. In my dreams I was being asked to do things that I could not possibly do, against impossible deadlines, often wearing only underwear, and in real life this identical theme played out day after day—except the underwear part.

Never had I been so spectacularly incompetent, so bad at everything I set out to do, for such a sustained period of time. I had never felt this way before. Truly, everything I had attempted prior to then, I had performed with a large measure of success. In college, back in Wisconsin, I had earned the respect of the English faculty, who had seen fit to name me teaching assistant my senior year. My ceramics instructor, finding that I had an affinity for it, put me in charge of firing the kiln each morning for my last year of college.

I had aced nursing school, despite my fear of math and science, and before that I had worked my way up from clerk to copy editor at the New York Daily Banner. I was beloved among the national desk staff—known as someone bright, reliable, who would come through in a clutch. The News Editor, my boss's boss, used to assign me tricky Page One captions to compose. *Me!*

People had always trusted in my basic competence, giving me a reason to believe in myself. How was it that I could suck so spectacularly at this?

No vital piece of equipment was ever where I expected it to be. No procedure that I undertook worked out the way it was supposed to. The foley catheter I placed in a woman on her way to the operating room for an emergency c-section got wound in the bed rails and was forcibly pulled out as we transferred her to the O.R. table. This rather painful experience caused her to scream as though being stabbed to death. She hoisted herself upright on the table and screamed, *"Get her out of here!,"* all the while pointing at me, her index finger trembling violently, the way someone on the witness stand points out her rapist at the defense table.

Another time, I was asked by my preceptor to shave a woman's pubic hair in preparation for a scheduled c-section after the "real" nurse placed the foley, took the vital signs, and completed the medical history form.

It was about 7:20 a.m. I had not slept well the night before—I kept dreaming about giving my preceptors overdoses of insulin while they were in labor—and I was still shivering from the cold of the locker room.

"Sarah's going to prep your abdomen for surgery now," said my preceptor, Laura. The patient, who preferred to speak Spanish, nodded, smiled meekly, and murmured a bashful "T'enkyew."

I pulled up her gown.

I could not even see her pubic hair, as it was completely covered by a large, firm roll of fat that hung down to the tops of her thighs.

Laura smiled tensely at me. I must have looked panicked. In only three weeks—after more than 30 years—my baseline facial expression had changed from mild disdain to naked terror. I looked at my face in the mirror, and I didn't recognize me any more.

With my left hand, I attempted to pull the fat-roll away from the pubes. I was marginally successful. I glimpsed the top of the pubic mound and dove for it with the gauze soaked in soapy water. When I released the roll to put down the gauze and pick up the razor, the target area vanished.

With my left thumb, I peeled back the roll and pulled it towards the patient's middle. As I began shaving off the top of the pubic hair, the roll of fat kept slipping from my fingers and seeping downward, like something viscous dripping from a bottle. My attention wandered. *Laura might be perfect, but she doesn't speak a lick of Spanish*, I thought. *I'll show her!*

"*Cuantos años tienen los otros niños?*" (How old are your other children?) The razor made a raspy sound in the stillness of the Anesthesia Prep Room.

"*El primer tiene cinco años, y el segundo tiene tres*," she replied. (The oldest is five and the other one is three.) *Scratch, scratch, scratch*, as I held her gaze firmly. *Fuck Laura*, I thought, scraping away confidently.

When I pulled the fat back again to evaluate my work, her entire lower abdomen was awash in blood. I must have nicked a small blood vessel near the skin. I glanced pleadingly at Laura, who was standing in the doorway.

"Uh, Laura?" She read the fear on my face.

"Oh, *shit!*" Laura caught herself too late. The words had already left her mouth.

The cesarean section had to be postponed until the razor-nicks healed. They were so deep there was a chance the patient could have developed a secondary infection if surgery was attempted the same day. Because what had occurred was extremely rare, and due more to bad luck than to bad skills, plus the fact that I was new and had a reputation for being "sensitive," I was only gently reprimanded and my orientation extended for another six weeks. With any luck, I might be off orientation in time to get my gold watch.

I spent most of the first two months crying in the bathroom. Really, it was a miracle that I had time to screw up anything, I was so busy sobbing in the stalls. One patient took a look at me as I entered her room with my preceptor and said aloud, "I don't want *her*. She's too hyper!"

By that time I was so sensitized that it only took a roll of the eyes from a patient, a "real" nurse or a resident to send me into the stalls. My eyelids remained permanently swollen, the skin around them blotchy and red. Steven said I looked like a burn victim.

"I'm really worried about you," Moe said. I was sitting on the toilet crying. She was standing at the mirror re-doing her eyeliner. It was three-thirty p.m. and we had four hours left of our shift.

"I mean it. I've never seen you like this."

I twisted a moist wad of toilet paper into a little spike and poked it into my right nostril. I had never known that a person could contain so much snot. It was apparently one of those body fluids that continuously replenished itself.

It didn't make it any easier that Moe wasn't suffering at all. Was she getting better assignments, or what? It wasn't fair. She was fine. Nothing terrible had befallen her or any of the patients assigned to her care.

I was certain I had made a massive mistake. I was afraid to tell this to anyone, even Moe. I felt like such an idiot! Not only was I incapable of doing this job that thousands of other adults did competently every day, but also everyone on the staff thought I was a complete nut case. Was it too late to turn back? I thought fondly of my cubicle at the Banner—my Rolodex, my phone headset, my computer. Was it possible they would take me back?

What was it I had longed for that had made me leave the Banner? I couldn't remember any more.

In the third month of my orientation, I had a delivery with Dr. Wallace.

Martin Wallace (a.k.a. "Wal-Mart," "The Wall") was a crusty, snarky, WASP-y old-fashioned Ob-Gyn, the loathsome kind who patronized his patients, called the nurses "Honey," and "Doll," and was generally regarded as a horse's ass. But everyone on the staff took great care to kiss his big horsey ass every chance they got, *"because he brings a great deal of money to this hospital,"* as one of the senior nurses sternly informed Moe when she pointed out what a disagreeable putz he was.

That day, Dr. Wallace's patient—my patient —was a big, robust Italian-American woman having her second child. She was about to get an epidural practically to her tits—it would probably be a real achievement if she continued to breathe on her own, actually. Dr. Wallace always insisted that his patients not feel any pain whatsoever.

I overheard him once answering a page from a patient in labor.

"Why should you suffer, dear? You just come right in and get your epidural."

I loved that—"*your* epidural." As though there was one especially made for every woman, with her name sewn into the lining, like your mom used to do for your camp stuff.

Dr. Wallace must have had some terrible nightmares to fear the birthing process so much. His c-section rate was about 60 percent. He could not bear for his patients to express the least amount of discomfort. He seemed convinced that if his patients felt no pain, they'd be less likely to sue him. Or maybe he was afraid they wouldn't *revere* him if they were allowed to feel pain. He nagged and harassed the poor anesthesiology residents to keep giving high doses of epidural medication to his patients to ensure their continued numbness. If they felt so much as the urge to pass gas, he was all over the anesthesia team, raving and criticizing.

Because of this, his patients routinely had foley catheters placed in their bladders during labor. After all, if you are given an epidural—which is meant to be given in advanced labor—at two centimeters, when you're barely contracting, the epidural will certainly slow down the process; thus, you're pretty much guaranteed to stay in labor at least sixteen more hours. During that time, you might need to pee a couple of times. But if you are numb to your tits, you might fail to notice the two or three liters of urine that have accumulated in your bladder.

Dr. Wallace loved doing cesarean sections. In his eyes, a cesarean resulted in a cleaner and more controllable outcome than those terrifying, messy, loud vaginal deliveries. Patients of his who had had prior cesareans and requested vaginal deliveries the second time around would be routinely talked out of it: "Oh, no, dear. It's too dangerous. We can't take the risk."

Dr. Wallace also used the patient's anesthetized state as a weapon against her. If he was in the mood to do a c-section on a patient who lacked a genuine indication for one, he would simply withhold epidural medication, telling the anesthesiologist to give no more doses.

I once heard him explain this to a patient as she screamed, "It's worn off! I need more! Give me more epidural! Please!"

Wallace: "No, dear, we can't give any more. You're too far along. It's not a good idea."

Liar.

Then, before you knew it, he was taking her to the O.R.

"We have to take the baby, dear," he would say, instead of, "I'm going to rip you open for no good reason at all."

Take the baby—I loved that. Where were we taking the baby? The zoo? The movies? ToysRUs? It sounded so heroic when he said it that way. I could almost hear the patient three months later gabbing with her friends at home:

"… and then they had to *take the baby*."

In addition to being full of shit, Dr. Wallace was hard of hearing. He wouldn't own up to it, and he could lip-read pretty well, but since he spent most of his working day in the O.R., where people are required to wear masks, it must have been torture for him. He could catch vowels, but consonants were not a part of his world any more.

"Are you ready to close?" one of the Ob/Gyn residents asked him once as they were finishing a c-section.

"What's that? My nose?"

The resident struggled mightily to be understood, miming the act of closing a door as she shouted, "*CLOSE? CLOSE? SHALL WE CLOSE?*" She pointed to the gaping incision and made sewing motions. The anesthesiologist was cracking up behind her mask; tears were starting to make their way down her cheeks.

"What's that? What are you saying?" Wal-Mart's forehead was purple with rage. He shook his big shaggy mane like a cartoon lion that has been hit on the head by a coconut.

I stood against the wall, observing in silence. Finally Suzie, the circulating nurse, pulled her mask to the side and yelled in his face:

"He wants to know if you're ready to *CLOSE!*"

One anesthesia resident, weary of the constant abuse, foolishly confronted the old man one day.

"Dr. Wallace, you can't expect that the patient will feel nothing. That's not realistic, and it's not safe to give that level of anesthesia for vaginal delivery."

"What did you say?" Big Wally reddened violently. They were standing in the hall outside the patient's room.

"What's that? What are you saying?" He towered over the resident, desperately trying to lipread.

"No, no, I didn't mean anything," the resident mumbled, blanching. He began backing away slowly, his eyes downcast, the way wilderness manuals advise you to do if confronted by a grizzly bear.

I wanted to tip the poor bastard off: "No, no, he really means it. *He wants to know what you're saying!*" but I stayed out of it. The resident cowered. Wal-Mart glowered.

They had reached a standoff. The resident was too intimidated to repeat what he had said, and Big Wally assumed the resident was defying him. Meanwhile, the resident could have been saying, "I felt up your grandmother in the movies last night," and the Wall would have been none the wiser, as long as he said it behind his hand.

"I won't discuss this with a *resident!*" he shouted. "Who is the attending supervising you? I'm paging him *right now!*" He stomped toward the nurses' station.

With more than two months' experience under my belt, I no longer threw up before leaving for work in the morning. I hardly ever had night-mares, and I had cut back to crying only every couple of days. My preceptors, desperate to pass me, had actually begun to entrust me with simple tasks. I had not done, strictly speaking, anything wrong—or even cried—for more than a week when I took on Mrs. Guarnaccia.

"It's about fucking *toyme*!" Mrs. Guarnaccia greeted the anesthesia resident. "I'm fucking *doying* here!"

I sat her up on the side of the bed, checked her blood pressure, checked the fetal heart-rate, held her in the proper position ("your back arched like an angry cat"), and mumbled comforting words as the anesthesiologists placed the epidural catheter and gave her the first, gigantic dose of medication.

Then I maneuvered her back to a lying-down position, replaced the fetal monitors on her belly and put the automatic blood pressure cuff on her arm. Mrs. G. rewarded my efforts by falling into a deep sleep. Her foley was draining buckets of urine, she was snoring powerfully, and her husband, a rabbity, diminutive man with thinning hair, multiple tattoos and the desperate man's 'do known as *the little tiny ponytail*, was watching baseball on the overhead TV.

So far, so good. Laura was leaving me alone, and Mrs. Guarnaccia had neither ordered me out of the room nor made disparaging comments about me. In fact, she seemed to like me. This was great! I was just like a "real" nurse in her eyes.

You're gonna make it after all.

Another of Dr. Wallace's annoying qualities was his need to deliver every one of his patients in the Operating Room. Instead of using the modern "birthing rooms" for the purpose for which they were designed, he stuck to his old-fashioned, 1960s ways. So when a Wallace patient was pushing and delivery was imminent, the poor nurse had to haul the bed, complete with screaming patient, down the long hallway to the O.R., set up the delivery table, attach the stirrups, call Pediatrics, and so on.

I had just offered Mrs. Guarnaccia some ice chips when she belched, moaned and began bearing down violently. I was alone in the room with her.

I glimpsed her husband in the hall.

"Sir!" I shouted. "Run to the nurses' station and get Laura!"

"Oh *SHIIIIIIIIT!*" Mrs. G. screamed. "It's coming! Where's my fucking doctor?"

I grabbed the bed, unplugged it, threw the IV bag on it and dragged it through the doorway.

Mrs. G. screamed:

"IT'S COMING OUT MY ASSHOLE! WHERE'S MY FUCKING DOCTOR? *IT'S COMING OUT MY ASSHOLE!*"

I ran past the nurses' station, shoving the bed frantically. Laura was paging Dr. Wallace. An Hasidic Jewish couple waiting to be triaged nodded and smiled politely as Mrs. G's invective filled the hallway like an aria.

I said a silent prayer: "Please, Lord Buddha, Baby Jesus, God—don't let him miss the delivery."

I had just helped her onto the delivery table when Wal-Mart showed up. He was all smiles.

"Ready? That's great, dear."

He went out to the scrub sink to wash up while I searched for the stirrups. Moe wandered in.

"Need help?"

"Where's Laura?"

"They have a STAT c-section across the hall. Everybody's there but me. Laura sent me to help you."

We each lifted a stirrup into the holes on the sides of the table. Mrs. Guarnaccia screamed intermittently, "Where *the fuck* is my doctor?" and "Get this *fucking* thing *out of me!*"

"Shhhhhhhhh! He's right outside," I reassured her.

Why wouldn't this fucking stirrup fit in this fucking hole?

Big Wally demanded a gown and gloves. We continued to wrassle with the stirrups. We could get them in the holes, but they wouldn't go all the way down. The table looked like a Picasso sculpture, out of his Blue Period.

"What's wrong with the stirrups? *I need those stirrups!*" The Wall shouted.

"It's coming out my asshole!" Mrs. Guarnaccia reminded us.

"You have them on the wrong sides! *Switch sides!*"

"It's coming out my asshole!"

Moe shrugged, yanked her stirrup out and ran around the front of the table to my side. I did the same with my stirrup. Sweating profusely, we nearly collided between Mrs. G's legs. Still we could not place them at the desired height. If Mrs. Guarnaccia had been a center in the N.B.A., she might have been able to reach the knee-gatches.

"What is *wrong* with you two? *I want a real nurse!* Where's Laura Bialecki?"

"It's fucking coming out! I fucking mean it!"

The baby shot out of Mrs. G. in the direction of Wallace's torso. One of Mrs. G's legs hung off the table, the other she pulled against her chest. Big Wally barely caught the kid, grabbing it by its arm and foot and dumping it onto the instrument table before clamping and cutting the cord. The baby, a girl, began bleating and peeing on the clamps and sterile drapes.

"Oh, my beautiful baby! Oh, thank you so much!" Mrs. G. was suddenly tearful. Loaded up with endorphins, she was suffused in a saffron aura.

Wally's face turned bright fuschia. With one hand he clasped the screaming baby's ankle; with the other, he pointed at the door.

"Get a *real nurse* in here right now!"

Without pausing for a crying break, after the delivery I cleaned Mrs. G's bottom, removed her foley catheter, transferred her to a stretcher, disassembled the delivery table, dumped the placenta into a plastic bucket, gave the baby her Vitamin K shot and eye ointment, filled out all the papers, got the baby started breastfeeding and took Mrs. G's vital signs every fifteen minutes. *So there.*

Fuck Wallace, anyway, I thought. *Everything's all right, nobody died.* Now that he was gone, I could relax and take care of the newest Italian-American princess and her mother.

"I think she fell asleep," Mrs. Guarnaccia said. I reached for the baby. She was gray and limp, her skin clammy.

Oh my God. This baby is dead.

I ran to the doorway, stuck my head into the hall and screamed, *"Call Peds now!"*

The baby weighed nearly ten pounds. Lifeless, with no muscle tone, she felt like a bag of rocks. I carried her unsteadily to the warmer and began rubbing her back. Nothing.

You are the first rescuer, ran through my head. *You are alone in the room.*

We had completed our two-day Neonatal Advanced Life Support (NALS) a couple of days before.

"What's wrong? What's wrong with my baby? What's the matter?" Mrs. Guarnaccia began to sob. Her husband appeared behind me without warning, staring over my shoulder.

"What's the matter with the baby?"

"Please, Mr. Garagiola, I'm begging you. Go to the nurses' station right now and tell them to *get in here!"* In my panic I had renamed him after a minor sports figure.

The baby had no discernible heartbeat, and she was making no effort to breathe.

I grabbed the suction catheter—thank God, it was still attached—and suctioned Lucia's mouth and nose.

I was praying to God: *"Lord, don't let her die. She's an innocent baby. People love her. She has a name. Her name is Lucia."*

I grabbed the infant ambu bag and placed the mask over her nose and mouth as we had been taught. *The important thing is to get a good seal between the mask and the baby's face, allowing no air to escape.* I opened the oxygen valve and began squeezing the bag. Her chest rose and fell with each puff, as the mannequin's had done.

I listened for a heartbeat. Still nothing. I began chest compressions as we had done on the infant model. *Compress the sternum rapidly, approximately 1 to 1 1/2 inches, with the index and third fingers or both thumbs.*

One-and-two-and-three-and-four-and-five—puff—one-and-two-and-three-and-four-and-five—puff—one-and-two-and-three-and-four-and-five --puff. On the third cycle, she stiffened, turning ghostly white, then pale pink. She began to cry weakly, moving her arms and legs.

"What's going on? What's going on?" Mrs. Guarnaccia was inconsolable.

"She's okay, Andrea," I shouted. "She's okay. I'll explain everything in a minute."

(If spontaneous respirations occur, stop chest compressions. Observe. Check heart rate. If above 100, and if spontaneous respirations continue, stop positive-pressure ventilation. Continue observation.)

Then Pediatrics barreled in, a huge crowd of them. Two anesthesiologists followed, joined by the charge nurse. Suddenly I had a roomful of people, where none had existed five minutes before. The baby was crying lustily.

"We'll admit her to the Observation Nursery, of course," the senior Peds resident said. "But it sounds like a vaso-vagal episode to me. Probably cold stress. She'll be fine."

(A *vaso-vagal episode* is what happens when a person experiences acute stress—such as having blood drawn if you are needle-phobic, or witnessing some terrible trauma—leading to a rapid drop in blood pressure. In adults, it manifests itself as cold sweats, a slow heartbeat, fainting, etc. In newborn infants, who are unable to regulate their body temperature, merely getting cold can trigger this response.)

"You're kidding me! So you mean she would have snapped out of it?"

"Maybe, maybe not. But you definitely did the right thing."

Before they took Lucia Guarnaccia to the Observation Nursery, they gave her to Andrea to hold. She sobbed.

"My poor little girl! My Lucia!" She looked over at me. "You! What's-your-name! Sarah! You saved my baby's life! *I love you!*" She reached for my hand and squeezed it. She had a powerful grip.

I wrenched my fingers from her hand and patted her cheek. I was feeling tearful myself.

"Oh, now, take it easy, Andrea. Everything's going to be okay."

"I mean it! You saved my baby's life! *You are a wonderful nurse*! I will never forget you!"

Dr. Wallace appeared.

"What's going on? Why wasn't I paged? What's wrong?"

He bristled with rage. Now I was going to have to *e-nun-ci-ate* in his face in front of this poor, terrified woman.

Andrea pulled herself upright on the stretcher, still holding the baby.

"You see this baby? Well, she stopped breathing and *she* saved her life! So *don't you yell at her!*"

Dr. Wallace was floored. He looked to the senior Pediatric resident for backup.

"It's true, Dr. Wallace. The baby had what seems to be a severe vaso-vagal episode and stopped breathing. This nurse resuscitated the baby by herself. By the time we got here, the baby was pink and crying. We're going to admit her for observation and do a sepsis work-up, chest X-ray, EKG and head film, but she looks fine."

Big Wally's eyebrows shot up. He said nothing; only patted Andrea's thigh absently and left.

"So," Moe said to me on the subway ride home. "Not with a whimper, but with a bang."

"What?"

"It's T.S. Eliot, doofus."

"Bitch, *I'm* the English major, did you forget? I know the quotation! Only you got it backwards, and how does it pertain to me?"

"Because your orientation has finally ended, not with a whimper—as in, defeat—but with a bang—as in, triumph! How does it feel, bitch?"

It felt great, to tell you the truth.

Crash

The "crash" c-section at NYCAS was a thing of beauty. It would usually start with either a *fetal bradycardia* (severe drop in the baby's heart rate) or a "bad" fetal scalp pH. [When you think a fetus might be in trouble but you're not sure, and if the mother is dilated enough, the Ob/Gyn resident might place a sterile cone in the mother's vagina, visualize the baby's head through the cervix, puncture the fetus' scalp with a tiny scalpel, and collect a few drops of blood. The lab then analyzes the blood for oxygen and pH (the balance between acid and base in the blood, giving an indication of the baby's oxygen status). A "bad" pH means the baby needs to be delivered *now*, by "crash" or STAT c-section.]

The prolapsed cord was another popular event at NYCAS, especially at night, for some reason. [A prolapsed cord occurs when the bag of waters (the "membranes") ruptures and instead of the fetus' head descending further into the cervix, a loop of the umbilical cord drops down. That little loop of cord, if compressed by the weight of the fetus above it, can create acute asphyxia, because if the cord is compressed, the baby can't get oxygen from the placenta. It's as if the baby is buried alive in a hermetically sealed coffin. A prolapsed cord calls for a crash c-section.]

Other c-sections were not crashes, and they were usually boring and tedious. A scheduled c-section, for example, was carried out in a very civilized manner—she showed up, we prepped her, placed a foley, obtained written consent, started her IV, she met with the anesthesiologist and we took her to the O.R.

Or sometimes a c-section was inevitable, but not a crash. If a woman couldn't push the baby out, for example, or if she stopped dilating and the fetus was stable, we took our time and did a calm, boring, regular old c-section.

But the crash section was a joy to behold. Never was there such a well-lubricated crisis machine as the NYCAS Labor & Delivery night team. Everyone had a job to do, and everyone did his or her job to perfection. The flinging of instruments, shouting of mild oaths and tossing of sterile towels and drapes across the operating table was preferred, but not required. The violent knocking over of garbage cans, laundry hampers, etc., as you "crashed" through the O.R. door with the bed was another endearing feature of the crash section. I loved it.

Whereas once I would panic when called upon to be the scrub nurse for a crash section, I now relished the opportunity. I was part of a team that saved lives. As the scrub nurse, all it took to triumph in a crash section was to get five minutes on the doctors. If you had five minutes to scrub, open the instruments and lay them out before the team came barreling in with the patient, you'd be fine.

What got my stomach churning was when you entered the O.R. at the same time as the docs. They'd invariably yell for things before you were ready to hand them over. It would turn into a shouting and instrument-flinging match. Meanwhile, there on the table lay the terrified patient—or the intoxicated patient, or the unconscious patient, or the hostile, combative patient, or the seizing patient.

It was 4 a.m. I had just admitted an Arabic-speaking patient in early labor. Through her sister, who spoke a small amount of English, I had managed to piece together a medical history of sorts. The patient attended the Ob/Gyn Clinic, she had arrived from Yemen two months ago, and she was having her third baby. We thought her due date was next week, but we were not sure.

Taking a history from someone who does not speak a language that you speak—especially at 4 a.m.—can be dicey as well as draining. It entails the use of "loud English" combined with intense facial expressions and body language. (Let's face it, anyone can be coerced into understanding loud English.)

Example:

(Loudly and slowly) "Do you have any … PROB-LEMS WITH YOUR *LIV-ER*? (Point to liver. Facial expression says, *God, I hope not.*)"

Translator mumbles something in Arabic.

Patient: "… Noooooo?"

"Okay. So do you have any PROB-LEMS WITH YOUR *HEART*? (Tap mid-chest area. Identical facial expression as above.)"

Translator mumbles something.

Patient: "… Noooooo?"

"Goooood … So, now, do you *SMOKE*?" (mimicking smoking).

Patient: "No?"

"DRINK?" (mimicking lifting a martini glass)

"No?"

"DRUGS?" (mimicking mainlining heroin while simultaneously puffing on a spliff)

(Patient too horrified, or mystified, to respond.)

"G-o-o-d! So, now. Have you had any … *PROB-LEMS WITH THIS PREGNANCY*?"* (point to her belly with hopeful facial expression).

(Patient is silent, with quizzical facial expression.)

"ANY PROB-LEMS WITH THIS PREGNANCY? You know … *HIGH BLOOD PRES-SURE? IN-FEC-TIONS? DI-A-BE-TES? PRE-TERM LA-BOR?"*

Translator mumbles something.
Patient: "… Nooooo …?"

"Okey-dokey! *Great!* Any *ALL-ER-GIES?*"
(This is one that you really need to get right.)
Patient: "… No …?"

"You're sure? No *ALL-ER-GIES?*" (Facial
expression more open now, permission-giving).
Translator completely stymied.
Patient: "… Yeeeeeeeesss …?"

"*What?* You have *ALLERGIES?* (Horrified
facial expression)
Patient: "… Noooooo … ?"

Fernando Lopez-Gonzalez, the good-natured,
zaftig "house attending" [the staff attending
Obstetrician/Gynecologist assigned to "cover the
house" that night, teaching the residents, caring
for the patients who attended the Clinic, etc.], appeared at the nurses' station.

"Any new admissions?"

"Yes, L-G [We called him L-G.]. We just admitted a patient in early labor. Dr. Rosenthal knows
about her. She's four cms, full-term, not ruptured,
good tracing … She speaks Arabic."

"I will examine her."

"You sure? Ruthie just did."

I stood in the doorway. Dr. Lopez-Gonzalez
seemed to be getting bigger by the day. He tried
to sit on the bed to examine the patient, but the
bed was too high. He fidgeted with the electric
bed controls. They were tricky sometimes.

"How do you make this bed go down?"

"Press the Down arrow in the middle, between the picture of the head and the feet."

The patient looked horrified. A large, hairy nameless man wearing no identification was leaning on her bed, trying to manipulate it with his left hand while he held his gloved, lubricated right hand aloft over her private parts like a torch or a lantern.

"L-G. Her name is Nadira. She's from Yemen."

"Oh. Yes. *Hello*, Nadira." The patient began scooching up the bed towards the wall. L-G continued to jab the buttons on the side of the bed with his left hand.

"How do you lower this goddamn bed?"

The buttons were jammed again. Lopez-Gonzalez had part of his right butt-cheek propped on the bed and was bracing his considerable bulk against the side trying to achieve vaginal-exam position. Nadira was now sitting cross-legged at the top of the bed, pulling the sheets over her head.

We persuaded Nadira to lie down, and Dr. Lopez-Gonzalez examined her. As he did so, clear amniotic fluid began to pour from her vagina—liters of it. It poured over his glove and ran past his elbow to the armpit.

"Oh my God! I've got cord. This is a breech. *I've got cord!*"

The baby was breech—bottom first—something Ruthie Rosenthal, the second-year resident, had failed to notice on her vaginal exam. Now that Lopez-Gonzalez had accidentally ruptured the membranes, we had a prolapsed cord.

I screamed to the clerk, Mrs. O'Donnell, at the nurses' station: "Page Ruthie! Page Peds! Tell Carmen to open up the O.R. right now!"

When you discover a prolapsed cord, you have to keep your hand in the patient's vagina. You must try to avoid touching the cord, which can easily go into spasm, but you must keep the *presenting part* (in this case, the baby's legs and bottom) elevated off the loop of cord. This means you, the examiner, must ride to the O.R. on the patient's bed, straddling her, while pushing up with your index and third fingers whatever fleshy part is trying to descend into the vagina.

Lopez-Gonzalez made a mighty effort and hoisted his frame onto the bed. Nadira was pale, looking as though she might lose consciousness. Her sister entered the room, gaping.

"You've got to tell her!" I screamed at the sister as I shaved Nadira's belly. Madeleine began putting in the foley. The anesthesiologist stood at Nadira's head, trying to get a medical history. Nadira was too terrified to even speak Arabic.

"Do you understand?" I pleaded with the sister. "We have to do an emergency cesarean *right now*! Can you tell her?"

The sister shrugged. Her English had expired.

"Let's go!" Lopez-Gonzalez screamed. "I've got *feet* in my hands! *Let's go!*"

Ruthie held the door open.

I pulled the foot of the bed while the Anesthesiology attending pushed the head. Lopez-Gonzalez' giant butt was in my face.

"Hey, who's going to scrub with Ruthie?" I asked him as we crashed through the O.R. door. "You can't move your hand!"

Lopez-Gonzalez spied the first-year resident, Emanuel Jean-Baptiste, helping Carmen, the scrub nurse.

"You! Jean-Baptiste! Switch places with me!"

"Huh?"

"Get up on this bed! Get a glove on! Now!"

They made the switch quickly. Lopez-Gonzalez jumped off the bed and went to scrub. The patient, lowered onto the O.R. table, still had no idea what was going on.

I ran out to the scrub sink.

"L-G, we've got to tell her what's going on! It's assault and battery if we don't!"

"Bullshit. This is to save her baby's life. She'll understand. *We go now!*"

He finished scrubbing and barged into the O.R.

"Put her to sleep *now!*"

"Not until I've asked her a couple of questions, Dr. Lopez-Gonzalez, and not until she signs a consent form. We've got to get an interpreter!" The anesthesiologist was adamant.

Under the sterile drapes, Jean-Baptiste was wagging his butt, as though trying to get lower. Carmen dropped a large stainless-steel retractor

111

on his sterilely-draped back as she readied the instrument tray. We heard a muffled, *"Ow!"*

I had an idea. I had seen this once, on a television show about an emergency room.

I put the O.R. telephone on speaker, dialed "O" and asked for an AT&T International operator who spoke Arabic.

"Ma'am, we've got an emergency. The lady needs an immediate c-section— we're in the operating room ready to go—and she doesn't speak English. Can you help us ask her some questions and explain to her that we have to put her to sleep and deliver her baby by c-section?"

The operator got a medical history—no liver problems, no heart problems, possible sulfa allergy—within a couple of minutes, explained the situation to Nadira, and she was put to sleep.

"Skin incision – 4:52!" Madeleine called out. I could hear Jean-Baptiste's panicked, muffled voice under the drapes and instrument trays as they opened Nadira's belly.

"Hurry up! It's coming down! Hurry up!"

Ruthie and Lopez-Gonzalez cut and yanked and manipulated and pulled out Nadira's little bluish baby boy, handing him to Peds to fix.

"Birth time – 4:54!" Madeleine yelled to the Anesthesiologist.

"Jeez, L-G," I said admiringly. *"Two minutes from skin to baby!"*

That's what we did.

Cric

Lucy was a pale, short, red-haired Irish-American girl, forty-one weeks pregnant with a breech fetus.

"Come, on, Lucy, it'll be all right," Cheryl said as she walked the sobbing girl to the O.R. I followed behind with Luis, Lucy's boyfriend, who was dwarfed by the extra-large paper scrubs we had found for him to wear.

"But I'm afraid!"

"What are you afraid of?"

"I'm afraid I'm going to die!"

"Don't be silly, Lucy, you're not going to die. You're going to have a baby. Try to stop crying, honey. It'll make it hard for you to breathe through your nose."

Dr. Jody Morgenstern, the anesthesiology attending on call that day, was known for his good hands. The entire Anesthesia team at NYCAS was generally swell, but Jody was on my personal short list of people in whose hands I would want my own life. Smart, capable, hefty, sarcastic and flirtatious, Dr. M. was a favorite among the nurses.

I backed into the O.R., my hands held aloft and dripping, just as Jody was putting away his equipment.

"I can't believe it. My first wet tap! Twice in a row! I guess we'll try spinal." Jody was sheepish.

[A "wet tap" is what happens when an anesthesiologist, attempting to place an epidural needle, goes too deep, into the spinal space. A small amount of *cerebrospinal fluid* leaks out of the needle (the eponymous "wetness"). After a wet tap you can try again, which Jody did, unsuccessfully. You can then try for spinal anesthesia, which is one layer deeper, but still allows the patient to be awake and breathing on her own for the surgery.]

I was the scrub nurse, assisting my friend Cheryl, an ambitious, tough-minded third-year Ob/Gyn resident, and Dr. Dov Benyamin, the Perinatal Fellow covering the house that day. [A Perinatal Fellow is someone who has finished his four-year Ob/Gyn residency and is studying for an additional two years before taking exams to become a high-risk obstetric specialist.]

Dr. Benyamin was Israeli. He had a reputation as something of a rake, and he always wore expensive after-shave—a habit I found deeply appealing. He flirted with the nurses incessantly, and, like many non-Americans, had absolutely no sense of personal space whatsoever. That arm's length between you and someone else's face that most Americans dutifully observe in all social intercourse did not exist for Dov. When he talked to you, you could practically see his tonsils.

I didn't mind. He was cute, and his after-shave was loaded with pheromones—those animal hormones that make you want to mount someone, anyone, in the middle of the road on your way to Mass.

Dov had been a combat surgeon in Israel, and loved telling stories about the battlefield operations, the bloody casualties, the "M*A*S*H"-like circumstances under which he worked during his conscription.

Jody and Suzette, the third-year anesthesiology resident, had finished the spinal and were strapping Lucy to the table, attaching the EKG electrodes and pulse oximeter to her exposed parts when I came to the table. Lucy was still sobbing intermittently, but the sounds were blunted by the oxygen mask. Dov, Cheryl and I stood wearily by the table, our arms folded in front of our sterile gowns, waiting.

"Ready to test?" Jody asked.

"Testing," said Dov. Cheryl pinched Lucy's skin with an Allis clamp.

"I FEEL THAT!" Lucy screamed.

"Try again," Jody said.

Cheryl pinched the opposite side.

"I FEEL THAT!"

"What do you feel?"

"I feel sharp instruments cutting into my flesh!"

Jody was puzzled.

"I'm pretty sure the spinal should be working," he said.

"Don't open me up like this," Lucy screamed. "I feel everything!"

Jody thought for a minute and said, "Okay, Lucy, we're going to put you to sleep."

I picked up the scalpel reflexively.

Jody injected sodium pentothal, a short-acting barbiturate, into Lucy's IV line, then succinylcholine, a short-acting paralyzing agent. I watched the fight go slowly out of her body.

Suzette propped Lucy's head back and placed the laryngoscope in her mouth and started poking the *endotracheal tube* down Lucy's throat.

Thirty seconds went by as Suzette poked and looked. She had a troubled expression.

"I don't see anything. No landmarks," she said to Jody. "Take a look."

Jody manipulated the scope.

"There's a lot of edema," Jody said. "Hand me the tube."

He poked the tube down Lucy's mouth a ways, then took it out again. It felt as though a great deal of time had elapsed.

"Bag her," he instructed Suzette.

Suzette placed the mask over Lucy's mouth and squeezed the ambu bag a couple of times.

Nobody spoke.

"Her airway is completely spasm'd," Suzette said. "Nothing is getting in."

116

"What are we doing, people?" Dov asked.

Jody tried again with the tube. Nobody moved or spoke for a minute.

The circulating nurse, Debbie, who had been fussing with the infant warming table the whole time, spoke up:

"What's going on with the pulse ox?"

The pulse oximeter, the machine that "reads" the patient's blood oxygen content through her skin, was making strange sounds. Instead of a steady, rapid, high-pitched bleep, bleep, bleep, mimicking Lucy's pulse, it was making urgent "*BLOOOOO*—IP! *BLOOOOO*-IP! *BLOOOOO*-IP*" sounds, very slowly and irregularly.

"She's slowing down," Suzette pronounced.

It was a strangely abstract way of saying that Lucy was starting to die. I glanced at Cheryl. Behind her mask, her face had no expression.

"What's the situation here, guys?" Dov asked.

"Maybe you should start the case," Jody said.

"Can you ventilate her or not?" Dov asked.

"Just start the case," Jody said. "At least get the baby out."

"And what about the mother?"

"I'll try to ventilate with the ambu."

"But you said she's in bronchospasm."

"Just start the case!"

Cheryl reached for the scalpel. Her hands were shaking, a coarse tremor that made it look as though she had Parkinson's disease. I held her wrist with my gloved hand to steady her.

"Just a minute here," Dov said. He disappeared behind the ether screen [the vertically hung drape that visually separated Lucy's head from her body].

"What are you doing?" Jody demanded.

"I'll cric her."

[A "cric" (pronounced "crike") is a cricothyrotomy—a temporary, emergency surgical slit in the throat, made slightly higher than an actual trache would be placed. None of us had ever seen one.]

"You've done this before?" Jody was skeptical.

"In the Israeli army? Are you kidding?"

Lucy began thrashing violently on the table.

"She's moving!" Cheryl shouted.

The medications had worn off and Lucy was awake.

Jody immediately dropped a nasotracheal tube in Lucy's nose, depriving Dov of an opportunity to do field surgery. [A nasotracheal tube can be placed "blind" if the patient is breathing, because you can follow the breath sounds until you know you are in the right place, unlike an endotracheal tube in the throat, where you must go by visual landmarks to ensure correct placement.]

Lucy was breathing raspily and flailing her arms and legs.

"Bag her now!" Jody ordered Suzette. "Start the case!" "he commanded Dov.

"Knife," Dov said.

I handed him the scalpel.

Lucy's blood was almost black, it was so oxygen-depleted. She bucked and thrashed as Dov made the skin incision.

"Can't you give her something?" Cheryl asked, horrified. "She's moving all over!"

"We're very glad she's moving!" Jody snapped back. "Why don't you infiltrate the layers with local as you go?"

Cheryl looked at me helplessly. I screamed to Debbie, "Get me Lidocaine! Get me a 20 cc syringe and an 18 gauge needle!"

My hands shook so badly I could barely draw up the anesthesia with the syringe. I handed it to Cheryl, who began injecting it into Lucy's uterus.

"Uterine incision!," I called out.

Lucy's blood vessels had clamped down so severely in trying to keep her alive that there was scarcely any blood at all when we opened her uterus.

The baby's body was gray. Cheryl worked her hand into the incision and wrestled its bottom out. It was a boy. She slapped his footsoles. He began to cry weakly as she handed him to Peds.

We finished the case in record time: Twenty-seven minutes from skin incision to skin closure. Lucy, awake now but sedated, breathed raspily and fought us weakly.

Afterwards, in the Recovery Room, Lucy said, "I'm so glad you decided to put me to sleep. It was so much better! Thank you so much!"

I looked at Jody, who was standing back watching Lucy. He shrugged.

"Thank God for Versed," he muttered. [Versed is a powerful benzodiazepene—related to Valium —that is routinely given to patients during a big operation. Not only a sedative, Versed has powerful amnesic properties as well. Patients who get Versed usually remember nothing of the actual surgery.]

He would tell the whole story to her later.

It was 6:30 a.m., and I had to come back again that night to work.

I went by the O.R. to finish cleaning the instruments. Dov was standing there, propped against the wall of the O.R., his head in his hands, clammy and exhausted. He had not spoken since we had taken Lucy to the Recovery Room.

"Dov, you would have really done that?"

"Sure," he said. "I've done it a million times." He stared at me as I began picking up the instruments to put in the sink. I could feel him staring at my ass as I turned away from him.

"What are you doing after the shift?"

"Me? What do you think I'm doing? I'm going home to sleep."

"Want to have breakfast first?"

Dov lived on the campus of the hospital, in a large, Stalinesque apartment block with low ceilings and ugly light fixtures. The carpeting in the narrow hallways was damp and stained with multiple, unidentifiable substances. I don't know how he had talked me into coming to his place instead of going out for breakfast.

I was standing by the dirty window of the living room, watching the boats on the Hudson, when Dov grabbed me from behind.

"Please," he murmured in my ear.

"Please?"

"Please. I want you so badly. Please."

I could feel his erection pressing against my back. He was small but powerfully built.

I could smell his aftershave. He licked my ear.

I shouldn't do this.

Crack

NYCAS Medical Center was the Mecca of high-risk obstetrics. Women with until-then-unnamed diseases got pregnant, came to NYCAS to deliver, and died on the operating table on a regular basis.

Women with rare pre-existing conditions that absolutely ruled out pregnancy came to NYCAS pregnant. A woman with *pulmonary hypertension*, told by her primary care physician, "If you ever get pregnant, you'll die," got pregnant, came to NYCAS, and died in the Recovery Room of Labor & Delivery. Women with diabetes of long standing, whose kidneys were severely compromised by all the years of diminished blood flow to them, who were advised that a pregnancy would finish them off, conceived—apparently without much effort—and arrived at NYCAS for care, with or without functioning kidneys. Women with lupus, severe heart defects, Hodgkin's disease—all of whom had undoubtedly been advised not to get pregnant—got pregnant and came to NYCAS to avail themselves of its high-risk obstetrical specialists.

The obstetrical population at NYCAS was not only high-risk by disease. It was high-risk by neighborhood.

Washington Heights was the epicenter of the illegal Dominican immigrant population. There was a commonly held belief among illegal Dominican immigrants: If you were the mother of a baby delivered on American soil—an American citizen—you could not be deported. The Immigration and Naturalization Service took great pains to shatter this myth day after day.

Because of their shaky immigration status, a great many of these women did not seek prenatal care until they were in labor. Thus many dangerous conditions of either the mother or the fetus were diagnosed at the time the woman was admitted to NYCAS in advanced labor.

Sometimes these women came to Labor & Delivery by ambulance, bleeding profusely and wearing anti-shock trousers thoughtfully placed by the EMTs. Sometimes they came with the baby's umbilical cord hanging out of their vagina. Sometimes the vaginal exam revealed two small, premature feet in the vagina.

Washington Heights was also the capital of the crack cocaine epidemic in New York.

Ah, crack cocaine! I first learned of it as a nursing student. One of the nurses in my Ob rotation at St. Adele's didn't know what it was—nor did I—and she asked the patient how to spell it.

"Is that with a K?" she inquired of the sleepy, cranky pregnant woman.

Many patients who delivered at NYCAS were high on crack cocaine. Those of us who had cared for heroin addicts in the past, myself included, fondly recalled caring for junkies. They were passive, subdued and polite, usually giving you several hours' warning when they were going to withdraw.

The euphemism was "get sick:"

"If I don't fix soon, I'm afraid I'm going to get sick."

They politely asked for methadone, or, if their participation in a methadone program could not be confirmed, Dilaudid. Junkies didn't want to withdraw, and they didn't want to subject us, their emergency health-care providers, to the ugly array of symptoms they were likely to experience if they withdrew. In the main, heroin addicts were thoughtful people—good citizens, if you will.

Crack cocaine addicts, on the other hand, were just nasty.

"What is your due date?"
(Silence.)
"Excuse me, Miss? What is your due date?"
"Fuck! *Leemeealone!*"

"I'm sorry, Miss? Please try to answer the questions? What is your due date? When is your baby due?"

"What the fuck, Miss! I tol' the other one already! I don't know! Can't you just *leemethefuckalone?*" (Pointedly turning over on the stretcher, presenting naked back to the interviewer.)

Or:
"What is your profession?"
"Huh?
"What do you do for a living?"
"What? *Leeme alone, Miss, I'm sleepy!*"
"I'm sorry, ma'am, I just have to complete this form here, if you could just help me out. What do you do for a living?"
"Fuck, miss—*I'm a crack whore, okay?*"

Or:
"What is your drug of choice?"
"What?"
"What drugs do you take on a regular basis?"
"Nothing, Miss. I don't take nothing. Why you got to ask me that?"
"Well, for the well-being of your baby, I need to know if any drugs are in your system."
"I used to smoke rock."
"Used to?"
"I quit. I'm clean."
"So, when is the last time you smoked rock?"
"Last night."

Or:

"When's the last time you ate or drank any-thing?"

"Ten o'clock."

"What did you eat?"

"A quarter-pounder with cheese."

"And what did you drink?"

"Gin."

Sometimes crack addicts who were withdrawing were merely sleepy, profane and cranky. Other times they were psychotic.

"Call Security *now!*" Madeleine screamed to O'Donnell, the receptionist, as she ran past the nurses' station. Spotting me, she blurted, "Can you help? She assaulted Caroline! Can you hold one of her legs?"

Too late.

In the Delivery Room a naked, pale, bleached-blond pregnant woman was crawling onto the instrument table. The delivery table that she had just vacated was soaked with blood. Dov, Nina Thompson, who was a third-year Ob/Gyn resi-dent, Philip Parker, my favorite anesthesiology resident until he died of a drug overdose, the staff midwife, Caroline, and three nurses stood by, their arms folded. There was nothing to be done.

Instruments crashed to the floor with a mu-sical clang as she crawled along the table. When she reached the edge she lowered herself to the floor and sat down. A small pool of pinkish liquid immediately appeared on the beige tiles and surrounded her bottom.

"She just ruptured membranes," Dov pronounced. He stared at me in the doorway. I flushed.

Since our initial breakfast quickie, Dov and I had had sporadic contact. He was no Steven, but sex was sex. He was exotic, great-smelling, and he had the sex drive of a jungle animal. Sometimes when we were on a shift together he'd follow me into the clean utility room and mash me against one of the carts, slipping his tongue into my mouth hastily and squeezing my breast. He'd rub his erection against me and mutter in Hebrew.

The fear of getting caught made it seem more interesting than it probably was. Of course, we never actually did the deed on Labor & Delivery—just lots of foreplay. But I had lived too long—or perhaps I had lived too hard, or perhaps I worked too hard—to just make out with a guy. I had to complete the act eventually, or explode. This made for some decent morning sex.

We'd leave the hospital separately, reluctant to be seen together, and I'd ring his doorbell four times. By the time I'd arrive at the door of his apartment, he'd have a huge erection, like a divining rod, standing out from the front of his scrub pants, and he'd have his shirt off.

He'd slip his tongue down my throat as soon as he opened the door, his coffee- and-cigarettes breath somewhat repellent at first. He'd pull me forcefully into the entryway, backing me against the wall. He would squeeze my butt-cheeks violently with his hands, as though trying to remove them.

We would make our slow, thumping way to the bedroom in this semi-blind fashion, a human Pushmipullyu, sometimes knocking into pictures on the wall or banging our hips into doorknobs. Foreplay? We'd already done that in the clean utility room several hours before.

I was still seeing Steven, but rarely. Now more than ever, I wanted a serious boyfriend, I wanted to have babies, I wanted a house or a condo, and Steven—Steven refused to grow up. We had simply outgrown each other.

Dov and I were tentatively on for a morning date after the shift that night. We didn't work together much, so it was an offer I couldn't refuse.

The patient arose from the floor and climbed onto the delivery table.

"Baby coming!"

Caroline, the midwife, approached the table warily. She was rumored to be in her seventies. She had been with the NYCAS Ob/Gyn department for more than 20 years. She looked frail, but she was strong as hell.

"Rozelle, if you kick me again, I'll walk out of here," she warned the patient.

A female Security guard arrived just then.

"Where's the others?" Dov asked.

"It's just me that came," she said.

"Oh, you'd better call in the rest of them," Dov said. *"Now!"*

Sure enough, the patient began to kick and buck on the table. Caroline stood back.

"I can see the baby's head," she shouted. "Somebody better help me." I wondered why Caroline, of all the personnel in the room, had been designated the deliverer. Why not Dov? Why not Nina?

Dov held one leg. Philip stood behind the table and held an oxygen mask over the patient's face— a good idea, as it somewhat muffled her cursing and screaming.

"What we call 'staff oxygen,' " Philip said to me, winking.

Nina, who weighed about 102 pounds, held the other leg. Every time the patient thrashed, lifting her legs, Nina went up in the air also.

The patient kicked at Caroline's face. Caroline leaped back. The baby's entire head was almost out.

"Where's Peds?" Dov demanded.

"I'll resuscitate the baby," Philip volunteered.

Caroline stood to the side, on the Dov-leg-side, gloved and gowned. I joined her. *Fuck these people. Letting a 70-year-old midwife deliver an hysterical crack addict all by herself! Fucking cowards!*

"Rozelle, if you hurt her again, I'll hurt *you*," I said.

Two male security guards wandered in.

"Need help?"

"Duh!" Nina intoned. On cue, she levitated as Rozelle lifted her legs straight up, making a low-pitched growling sound.

The baby hit Caroline in the upper abdomen. Dov struggled to hold the left leg in place. Caroline clamped and cut the cord—the baby was mewling and grimacing, but its skin was purplish-gray—and took the baby to the warming table for Philip to resuscitate.

"Get a cord gas!" Dov reminded Caroline. [A cord gas was a test of the pH of the blood in the umbilical cord. The pH gave you a ballpark idea of the baby's oxygen status at the time of birth.]

"Oh, my baby! What is it? A boy?" Rozelle craned her neck on the delivery table. "Oh, thank you, Miss! Thank you so much! I'm sorry if I acted bad!"

"There, now," said the female security guard, patting the patient's leg. "You did fine."

"Don't tell her that!" I screamed. "She assaulted Caroline! You should arrest her!"

"Oh, never mind, Sarah," Caroline said to me. "Thanks for your help." She peered at Rozelle's bottom.

"Caroline, I have two words for you," Dov said. *"Secondary intention."*

Secondary intention is the way that lacerations heal when they're not stitched together. Dov was suggesting that, if Rozelle had a vaginal laceration, Caroline should leave it alone.

"It's a deep second-degree," Caroline said, poking gingerly at the woman's flesh. "It needs sewing. It's bleeding."

"Owwww, miss, what are you doing?" Rozelle again thrashed on the table, pulling one leg out of Nina's grasp. "Tha'shit hurts!"

"I need to repair your vagina," Caroline said. "Or else you could bleed to death."

"I don't care, miss, I just need to sleep now. *Leeeme alone!* Why you can't fix it later?"

Philip ended up giving Rozelle deep sedation—nitrous oxide through a mask —to allow Caroline to repair the laceration. It was the anesthetic equivalent of giving general anesthesia for a Pap smear.

No one offered to help Caroline.

The baby's cord pH was 6.99. A normal human blood pH should be between 7.35 and 7.45—an extremely narrow range. The baby's blood was severely *acidotic*, indicating that he had been oxygen-deprived for a good while.

"Here, take him for a sec," Madeleine said. She was cleaning off the baby warmer and getting the infant transporter ready, so that Peds could take the baby to the Observation Nursery. She handed me the baby.

He was a homely, skinny little guy with a huge head, a receding hairline, reddish hair and big bug-eyes. Who would hug this baby? Who would love this baby? He would become another "boarder baby," living in the Newborn Nursery long after he had ceased to be a newborn, in a crib too small, with nothing but a mobile to distract him and a parade of volunteers, nurses and infant care technicians to hold him for feedings, swaddled tightly, four times during the day and twice at night. Who would read to him? Who would make up nicknames for him, or talk to him in cartoon voices to make him stop crying?

I imagined NYCAS as a factory, looming alongside the Hudson, with little crack babies shooting out of smokestacks all day long.

Who was going to adopt this kid? God knows, crack babies were hard to love. They were extremely irritable, needing to be wrapped tightly and left alone most of the time. Too much stimulation caused them to scream and flail and spit up. Even a simple diaper change would cause this baby to cry hoarsely, inconsolably, kicking his scrawny legs and arching his back in outrage.

Rozelle woke up abruptly and saw me.

Sitting up on the table, she held out her arms without speaking. For a minute, she resembled a regular mom.

I looked at Madeleine. She shrugged.

I put the baby in her arms. She would probably never hold him again. Tears dripped down her cheeks.

"His name is Duncan," she said.

What We Say to Patients ...

About 70 percent of the pregnant patients we cared for at NYCAS Medical Center were immigrants from the Dominican Republic. Astoundingly poor, often illegal, sometimes illiterate, they had somehow convinced themselves that living in rented rooms without windows in urine-scented tenements where gunshots could be heard nightly in the courtyard afforded a brighter future than did life in their tiny, dusty country.

Learning English was not an urgent priority for these women, given the far greater urgency of paying for a few meals a day and keeping up with the rent.

Indigence and ignominy do not necessarily breed patience, thoughtfulness and understanding.

Thus many Spanish-speaking patients expected the overworked staff of NYCAS to speak Spanish all the time. If you didn't speak Spanish, if your accent was off, if your pronunciation was poor, if you struggled to remember words, you got the immediate Bugs Bunny sign.

The Bugs Bunny sign is when the patient squinches her eyes in frustration, lifting her nose and upper lip several times in rapid succession, like a rabbit.

The Bugs Bunny sign, to me, was an expression of the impatience that is born of bone-weariness. When you saw the Bugs Bunny sign, you saw the patient's thoughts:

Another one who doesn't speak Spanish!

Sometimes at the end of a 12-hour night shift at NYCAS, when a patient would wander up to the nurses' station with an expression that was both hopeful and wary, I would address her in English. My Spanish would have plumb run out, as though siphoned from me, and there would be nothing but English words clanging around in the bottom of the tank.

"How may we help you?"

Pause.

Bugs Bunny sign.

Pause.

Then I would reach down deep and pull out a couple of phrases:

"Porque veniste aqui esta noche?" (Why did you come here tonight?)

"Peng" (Pain).

Although the patient might be hiding a few words of English deep in her cerebral cortex, we would never hear a single word of English out of her after that.

In our struggle to be understood, sometimes we succeeded brilliantly. Other times we failed.

One night Madeleine asked a patient when she *last ate her husband*. (The intended question was a combination of "when did you last eat?" and "where did your husband go?")

This blunder put the patient in a state of high Bugs Bunny alert. Her entire nose, eyebrows, forehead, cheeks—all her features—twitched like mad.

"Looked like she was about to have a seizure," Madeleine muttered after I explained her error.

Another time I asked a patient whether she had *pain in her beer*:

"Tiene dolor en la cerveza?" (*Cabeza* = head; *cerveza* = beer)

Yet another time, I inquired with great disdain whether a patient had taken "Christmas lessons."

Christmas is "La Navidad," you see, and *"Natal"* is the Latin root for childbirth. In my haste to be sarcastic, I melded the two somehow, and "las clases de Navidad" urped out of my mouth, hovering in the air like a tiny, ugly insect.

Like English lessons, childbirth preparation classes were not foremost on the needs lists of our poorest patients. Preparation? That was a foreign concept.

The WIC program, which gave needy pregnant women "checks" to redeem at grocery stores for free blocks of yellow cheese, generic Cheerios, bread, whole milk, infant formula, canned goods and other items, was intractable when it came to issuing more than one check in a calendar month. More often than not, the WIC items ran out before the calendar did. The social worker in the Ob/ Gyn clinic routinely referred our patients to food banks in midtown Manhattan. Sometimes we nurses brought in our old winter coats for the social worker to give to those patients who arrived at the clinic deep winter wearing several layers of cotton t-shirts and an orlon sweater as outerwear.

The nurses in the clinic constantly advised their pregnant patients to attend the free, Spanish-speaking childbirth preparation classes offered by the hospital, and the patients constantly declined.

So I was pretty much asking a rhetorical question about the Christmas lessons. The patient, a first-timer whose "boyfriend" had given her gonorrhea, chlamydia and trichomonas (common, treatable sexually transmitted infections) during the pregnancy, had just made some query in Spanish about labor that was so mind-blowingly ignorant that I had to comment on it—something along the lines of 'what hole does the baby come out of?'

I shot back with: "No atendaste las clases de Navidad?" (You didn't take the Christmas lessons?)

That'll teach her!

If one is going to be sarcastic and rude in another language, one really ought to have a better command of that language.

My friend Cheryl, an Ob/Gyn resident, once shouted to a woman who was being prepped for a crash c-section:

"Hace un suero para dar el flujo! Necesito cesaria ahora!" ([He/she/it] makes an IV to give the mucus! I need a cesarean *now!*")

Another time I asked a patient if she had "any Indians with diabetes." This elicited a veritable Bugs Bunny marathon.

I couldn't figure out why. I tried again:

"Tiene algunas prietas con diabetes?" ("Do you have any Indians with diabetes?")

I meant to say "cousins" or "relatives" with diabetes. *Prima* is "cousin." I'm not even sure why or how I knew the Spanish word for "Indian"—*prieta*.

References to "caca" and "poo-poo" were popular in our unit. After all, the act of pushing the baby out was most like taking a dump. We could manage to convey that concept, even if our Spanish was not perfect..

Thus: *"¡Empuje! Empuje!¡Empuje como caca!"* (Push! Push! Push like shit!)

Or: *"¡Estrenimiento!¡Estrenimiento!"* (Constipation! Constipation!)

One day Moe wanted to order oxtail soup from El Rey, the neighborhood dive. She didn't know how to ask for oxtail soup in Spanish, so she asked me to ask a patient how to say it.

"*Por favor, senora. Como se dice … Sopa. Sopa,*" I began. (Please, Madam. How do you say … Soup. Soup.)

"*Si? Sopa?*" (Yes? Soup?) The patient's mother was eager to help.

"*Como se dice … *" (How do you say…) … *sopa de …*" (soup of…)

I looked at Moe in desperation. "How do I say it?"

Helpfully, Moe began to gallop around the room, making little wiggly horns by her forehead with her fingers. She snorted like a bull.

"*Sopa de … de toro?*" (Soup of … of bull?)

No response.

Moe galloped back and forth, snorting and waggling her horns.

The senora was stymied.

"*Sopa de … nalgas do toro?*" (Soup of ass of bull?)

The senora looked horrified.

"*Sopa de cadera de toro?*" (Soup of hips of bull?)

Finally Moe de-horned herself, using her arm to make a perky little tail instead. She waggled her "tail" back and forth by her butt, snorting hopefully and galloping in place.

"*Sopa de … de… de … *" (Soup of … of … of…)

"*Diarrea?*" the senora asked. (Diarrhea?)

"Moe," I said. "You ain't gettin' oxtail soup today."

... And What They Say to Us

If we struggled mightily to be understood by our patients, our English-speaking patients struggled likewise to communicate in our language—the peculiar, Latinate vernacular of obstetrics and medicine.

It didn't always work out.

1. "I have fireballs on my Eucharist."

2. "My wife is leaking music from her vagina."

3. "I was seen in the Infidelity Clinic."

4. "I had an emergency c-section. My placenta exploded!"

5. "Don't give me no blood confusion!"

6. "I want to move my vowels."

7. "I'm here to be seduced."

8. "I take Ferocious Sulfate."

9. "The sonogram said my placenta has legs."

10. "The sonogram said my lining is low."

11. "I'm bleeding from my Amos."

12. "I had emotional diabetes."

13. "I have sick-as-hell anemia."

14. "I had the jelly thing."

15. "I'm passing blood clogs."

16. "I'm discharging."

17. "I'm trinkling."

18. "I have a puberty bump."

19. "I didn't see my ministration/administration."

20. "I didn't drink my pills ...

21. ... and then my period didn't come down ...

22. ... and *I came up pregnant.*" (var.: " ... *came out pregnant.*")

23. "Can they see the gentiles at 20 weeks?"

24. "I'm a very nutritious person."

25. "I was being treated for chlamydia, and then I *had a relapse.*"

26. "They said my Playtex was low."

27. "I have gas-stational diabetes

28. "I have placenta primavera."

29. "Good news! The tumor is not malicious."

Answers:

1. ... fibroids [benign growths] on my uterus.

2. ... mucus

3. ... Infertility Clinic

4. ... Probably her placenta *abrupted*, or detached itself from the wall of the uterus, a true obstetrical emergency

5. transfusion.

6. ... move my bowels. (Or she was talking about Scrabble – not clear.)

7. ... induced, as in *induced labor*.

8. ... *ferrous* sulfate, a generic iron supplement.

9. Placental *lakes* are small cavities in the placenta filled with fluid.

10. Jury still out on this one, but probably she was told she had a *low-lying placenta*, in which the placenta almost, but not quite, covers the opening of the uterus, or *cervix*.

11. ... anus?

12. ??????

13. … sickle-cell anemia.

14. ??? Something to do with the "mucus plug," the slimy bloody thing women sometimes pass from the vagina before they go into labor??

15. … clots. "Clogs" are the smallest kind. Medium-sized clots are called "clotches," and very large ones are called "clocks" or "blood clocks."

16. … having vaginal discharge.

17. ??? Leaking fluid? As in … the water broke? A combination of *trickling* and *sprinkling?*

18. ???????

19. …. menstruation, or menstrual period

20. … birth control pills …

21. … I didn't get my period ….

22. … found out I was pregnant.

23. Referring to a sonogram done on the fetus at the 20th week of pregnancy—can the baby's *genitals* be seen?

24. ?? a person practicing good nutrition?; possibly, a delicious person?

25. … boinked the infected guy again?

26. ???????? possibly *platelets*, components of blood that help with clotting

27. . ."gestational," or pregnancy-induced, diabetes. (*"Fill 'er up … with sugar!"*)

28. A mouth-watering main course made with fresh placentas …. Naw … she meant *placenta previa*, in which the entire cervix is covered by the placenta (see No. 13.).

29. … malignant.

Slow Code

"Sarah, page Anesthesia for an epidural in Room 2," Cheryl said.

I looked up from the patient's chart.

"You're kidding," I said. "She's eight cms, it's her third baby. She'll cough and it'll come out. Why are we wasting her time with an epidural?"

"Just page them, please," Cheryl said, avoiding eye contact.

Weird.

Almost as soon as the epidural was placed, the patient, Betzaida G., began bearing down.

"Quisiera hacer caca," she said politely (I would like to make poo-poo.).

"Cheryl," I yelled, "she wants to push."

Cheryl, looking sheepish, appeared in the doorway with the house attending, the imperious Dr. Anna Lieberman.

Anna was a young, attractive blond woman, Harvard-educated, who on paper seemed to have a perfect life—an adorable husband, a sweet little daughter, and a lofty position as Director of Obstetric Operations at NYCAS, reporting to the Chairman himself. Yet her every pore exuded unhappiness and hostility.

I wondered about this. How could someone have everything, yet be so unhappy? What if I got what I wanted—survived being a nurse, and got through midwifery school, and became a midwife—and still longed for something more?

None of the nurses could stand Anna. She seemed to regard us as simple multi-celled animals, unable to read or write, but capable of making annoying barnyard sounds and getting in her way. She was actually known to reply to nurses' occasional questioning with, *"Because I'm the doctor. That's why!"*

When addressing a nurse or junior resident, her words were forced out in impossibly low tones between tightly compressed lips and clenched teeth, as though she had lockjaw. Sarcasm was her m.o. She squeezed out each syllable in painfully slow fashion, as though the speakee was incapable of comprehending regular-speed English.

No one could figure it out.

"Per-haps she for-got to re-charge her vi-bra-tor," Moe said once, in a perfect Anna *sotto voce*, making like a ventriloquist.

"I think it's that her hus-band does-n't give it to her on the reg-u-lar," Debbie suggested, barely moving her lips.

"A second gown, please," said Dr. L. "And size six and a half gloves. Brown." [Brown gloves were the latest big thing among the attendings. They were meant to be hypo-allergenic, and suddenly everyone seemed to have a problem with the regular old white gloves. If you wanted to sound even more important, you demanded brown gloves. Moreover, there was a brown-gloves pecking order. Residents never asked for brown gloves. It was, apparently, frowned upon. Residents were not important enough to have developed skin reactions to white gloves yet.]

I fastened Dr. L.'s gown at the back. What was going on? Although the attendings liked to be present for the deliveries, they seldom scrubbed in, preferring instead to barge in without introducing themselves and stand against the wall throughout the delivery, steadily criticizing the residents' technique. Why was Her Majesty soiling her hands for an uncomplicated patient who has already delivered two babies vaginally?

"Straight cath, please," Dr. L. said sternly and oh-so-slowly.

I dropped the catheter on the table.

"Emp-ty the blad-der," she commanded Cheryl.

What was going on?

"Sarah," Cheryl said quietly. "Will you please get a pair of Elliotts forceps from the O.R.?"

"What?"

"Right away, please," Dr. L. snapped.

"Will you help me?" I asked Karen, the charge nurse. "I've been asked for Elliotts forceps and I have no idea where to look for them."

"Check the O.R.," Karen suggested. "The cabinet where the instrument trays are. They should be labeled clearly."

As an afterthought, she added, "What's going on?"

"I got no idea," I said.

The forceps clanged ominously against the smaller instruments on the table.

"Right blade," Dr. L. said quietly.

Cheryl grasped the giant spoon tentatively.

"Hold it in your left hand. Put your right hand in the vagina. Now transfer the blade to your right hand. Slide it alongside the head. Go lateral."

"Que haces?" Betzaida demanded. (What are you doing?) Her voice rose to a high-pitched yowl as Cheryl inserted the giant blade in her vagina. Her body lurched and flailed in the bed. She sounded like a cat whose tail had been stepped on.

"Ay, ay, ay, Dios mio!" (Oh my God!) Clearly her epidural was not strong enough to take away the sensation of having her vagina pried open with blunt instruments.

"Talk to her," Dr. L. ordered Cheryl.

"Senora," Cheryl began. *"Necesito hacer los forceps,"* (Ma'am. I need to make the forceps.)

"*Que? For-say?*" Betzaida screamed. "*Que me haces?*" (What? 'Forceps'? What are you doing to me?)

"Sarah?" Cheryl turned to me. "Can you help us out here?"

"I don't know how to say what you're doing," I said, "And I don't know why you're doing it, more to the point."

"*Just do your job and translate!*" Anna spat at me in regular speed.

They don't understand Spanish as well as I do, I thought. Perhaps I should say, "*Betzaida, esos pende-jos quieran lastimarte. Salga en seguida!*" (Betzaida, these assholes want to hurt you. Bust a move *now!*)

Instead I said, "I don't know how to say what you're asking." I hunched over the chart. Anna glared at me. I glared back.

As Betzaida howled and thrashed in the bed, Cheryl placed the left blade, Dr. L. criticizing her in frosty undertones all the while. Cheryl injected local anesthesia in Betzaida's bottom, cut a massive episiotomy, and the baby was lifted up and out, rather inelegantly, by the salad spoons, as nurses and lay people called them.

"What the hell was that all about?" I whispered to Cheryl after Dr. L. had left the room.

"Just never mind, Sarah," Cheryl said sternly. "Don't do this to me, please." She swatted her hand at me as if I were an annoying bug.

Within a few weeks, many nurses began to report similar experiences. It wasn't just Cheryl, and it wasn't just Anna. All the senior residents—Nina Thompson, Peter Liu, Katie Madden, Rob McDermott—would show up for the most un-complicated deliveries, pushing the interns and second-years out of the way, and then the house attending *du jour*—Lopez-Gonzalez, Dov, Karen Noble—any of them—would waltz in, demanding gowns, brown gloves and Elliotts or Simpsons forceps.

"My patient got a third," Maddie said dis-gustedly. "Imagine! A Para 3 with a third!" ["A third" was a third-degree laceration: when the *perineum*—the tissue between the vagina and rec-tum—tore spontaneously into the rectum itself, or an episiotomy tore through (*extended*) to the rec-tal muscle. A third-degree laceration or extension was something you might see in a first delivery, but women who'd already pushed out a baby or two seldom tore at all—certainly not severely.]

"Let's talk to the Prime Minister," Karen sug-gested. The Prime Minister was our nickname for the Ob/Gyn Chairman, Dr. Manning, a tall, be-spectacled, rail-thin New Englander who resem-bled T.S. Eliot.

"Are you out of your mind? He'll kill us! Besides, he doesn't talk to *nurses*," Debbie pointed out.

"I disagree," I said. "This is about patient care. He needs to know that patients are being forced to have unnecessary procedures for no reason."

"Let's just see what happens," Debbie said. "If it continues, maybe we'll approach him."

Two days later, when Nina Thompson asked me for Simpsons forceps for a Para 0 who had only been pushing for about fifteen minutes, I lost it.

"I need to talk to you, Nina," I said.

"Not now."

"Yes, now. Outside."

In the hallway I accosted her.

"What the hell is going on? Why are you putting forceps on that poor baby's head for no reason?"

"Dr. Benyamin is going to show me how to do an outlet forceps delivery." She sighed. On cue, Dov appeared.

"What's the trouble?" he asked.

"But what's the indication?" I asked, ignoring Dov. ["Indication" is a fancy medical way of saying "reason."]

"I—I—we all need to learn to do forceps. I could save a baby's life some day."

"But you don't need to do them on this baby!"

"Sarah, please," Dov said. "Don't get involved in this."

Dov and I were still seeing each other, although our encounters were infrequent. It was rumored that he was seeing a nurse who worked in the O.R. I wasn't sure how I was supposed to feel about that. It was ridiculous to feel jealous, but I did anyway. Why wasn't I good enough?

"Look. If we don't learn how to do them when they're *not* indicated, when it's easy," Nina pleaded, "we'll never be able to do them when they *are* indicated. Just get 'em, please."

Nina went into the patient's room.

"I'm calling Manning," I said.

"Are you out of your mind? Don't do that!" Dov began backing into the room, staring me down.

"Why not? He needs to know about this."

"Don't call him, you idiot," he hissed. "This will die down soon. This happens every year."

"What do you mean?"

"Every June and July, when the senior residents are about to graduate and the faculty realizes they don't know how to do a forceps delivery. It'll be over soon," he said.

"What are we doing about this?" Moe demanded. She, Karen, Debbie and I were across the street from the hospital, at our favorite Dominican coffee shop, having beer and eggs after our 12-hour night shift. Odd as it may seem, ice-cold beer tastes mighty good at 8 a.m., especially with fatty foods. Besides, it was good for sleeping during the daytime. The owner knew us by name, and usually greeted us by slamming the sweating Corona bottles onto the table with a big smile as we seated ourselves. I had been the nurse for the delivery of his daughter three months before.

"I think if we want to keep our jobs, we have to just go along," Debbie said.

"I'm not going along with this," I said. "This is about patient care. This is abuse. We're supposed to be patient advocates!" (I had a sudden flashback to my conversation with enthusiastic, high-pitched blond Kelly, surgical nurse, at the beer joint on the Upper West Side the night Steven had brought me to orgasm under the table with his finger.)

"Well," Karen said. "All I know is, it takes me a hell of a long time to find the suckers sometimes." She scraped her knife along the edge of her plate, then picked up her Corona and drained it.

"Find what suckers?" Moe inquired.

"The forceps, dummy. They're all jumbled together in the O.R. I can't always read Carmen's writing on the tape, can you? Don't you find it's really difficult to sort them all out? Plus, we have to really look carefully and make sure they've been properly sterilized." Karen stared steadily at Moe.

"You mean, like a slow code?" Moe asked.

"I don't know what you're talking about," Karen replied, "and keep your voice down. Let's get the check."

A "slow code" was definitely unethical, but it took place in many hospitals. When a patient was at the end stage of some terminal illness, with no hope of "intact survival," but the family stubbornly refused to sign the "do not resuscitate" order, sometimes the code team staged a "slow code"—meaning, everyone took his or her sweet time getting there after the code was called. Sometimes the team would arrive so late that its resuscitative efforts were futile, and the patient expired.

Nobody ever talked about this out loud.

"Damn, I can't find them," I muttered to Carmen.

I was in the O.R. after a pair of Elliotts forceps.

"What do you need?" Carmen inquired helpfully.

"No, don't bother. I see them," I said. I grabbed a set marked "Pipers" and strolled out of the O.R. Fortunately, the Ob/Gyn department didn't own enough pairs of forceps to keep them in each birthing room. Because they had only one or two pairs of each kind, they were all kept in a central place—the O.R.

I stopped by the nurses' station. Wendy, Julie and Karen were looking at a men's swimwear catalog.

"Hey, Wendy," I yelled, holding the wrapped instruments aloft. "Are these Elliotts?"

"Oh, golly, Sarah. I can't see from here. I don't have my glasses. Can you bring them over here to me?

"Sure, Wendy. Let me come around there to you."

I went around the long way—past the O.R.—and came out on the other side of the nurses' station.

"Here. What do you think?" I offered the package marked "Pipers."

"Hmmm ... I don't know. Looks okay to me. Karen?"

"Oh, silly Sarah, you simpleton!" Karen scolded me. "Those are *Pipers,* you doof! For a breech baby! Bad Sarah! Now go back and get the proper ones *STAT!*"

I ambled back to the O.R. I felt a little queasy. I could theoretically be fired for this.

"Carmen, I grabbed the wrong ones. Where are the—what did they want anyway? I've forgotten—was it Simpsons?"

"Elliotts?" Carmen said. Her face had a puzzled expression. "Here they are."

I stopped by the nurses' station again. I waved the Elliotts in the air.

"Here they are! Oops—I've dropped them!" I shouted as they landed with a clang. "I hope I didn't damage them!"

"Please – be - more - care-ful - next - time," Karen said sternly, her teeth clenched á la Anna Lieberman.

As I approached Room 1, Karen Noble stuck her head out the door, impatient.

"Come on! Where are they? The baby's almost out!"

"Oh, I'm so sorry," I said. "I had a bit of trouble finding them. We use them so often now—it's hard to know where to look." I tripped on my shoe cover and grabbed the wall with one hand. The package clanged to the floor.

"Are you all right?"

"Oh, sure," I said, picking up the instruments slowly. "But my back is killing me."

"Hurry up!"

By the time I got into the room and clumsily opened the blades, nearly dropping them for a third time, Marcy K., a 25 year old Para 2, had delivered two-thirds of her baby's head without assistance.

The rest of the baby squirted out, on cue, as I dropped the forceps on the table.

As Dov had predicted, the forceps teaching marathon ended abruptly in August, after the chief residents graduated and moved on. Anna confronted me by the nurses' lounge one day soon after.

"I know about your little plot," she said slowly, through clenched teeth. Her lips were white.

"What are you talking about?" my face turned bright red. I felt nauseated.

"I know how you tried to stop the residents using forceps. You could get in serious trouble for this."

"Dr. Lieberman, I have no idea what you're talking about, but I don't like your tone," I said, feigning outrage.

"Never mind. I'm going to let it go," she pronounced slowly. She turned and walked away.

Because I'm the doctor. That's why.

Dov

"Scream if you want to," Dov said hoarsely as he plumbed me. Our sweat soaked the bedsheets.

Sex with Dov was no epiphany, as it had been with Steven at the beginning, but it was strangely satisfying.

Consider the way large female mammals, in estrus, rub themselves recklessly against trees, rocks, fences, shamelessly.

The thing was—obstetrics, at least the way we did it at NYCAS, was sexy.

Let's face it. A crash section is sexy. Emergencies are sexy. And Labor & Delivery at NYCAS was all about emergencies.

Some situations were daunting, of course, and panicky: *Would-we-get-her-to-the-O.R.-in-time?*, etc. But we were so good at it, and the familiar rhythms of the frantic music we stepped to were both comforting and provocative. The wordless communication; the dovetailing of vital tasks; the urgent shouting across the patient's bed; the occasional hasty words of comfort flung at the patient; the lightning speed with which the preparatory work was accomplished, and the slapdash, luge-like race down the narrow hallway to the O.R.—it awakened primitive urges in me.

We were saving lives. It was almost disappointing for me to pass a night at NYCAS without a three-alarm crisis.

Was there something wrong with me? Was I a sexual deviant?

But if I was, Dov was too.

Before crash sections, as overheated bodies jammed around the patient's bed, Dov sometimes deliberately stood behind me, jamming his pelvis into my butt for no particular purpose. Smelling his after-shave, his sweat, his unwashed hair made me flushed and dizzy with sexual longing. Was it me provoking his erection, or was it the situation?

"Scream if you want to," he said again, pulling back from me to look at my face. He licked my ear.

I hated that.

It was 9:30 a.m. I had just finished an exhausting shift and I was starving. We had not bothered with breakfast this time. Dov's curtainless, streaky windows were open to the courtyard below, and I could hear the shouts of children splashing in an inflatable pool.

If we could hear them, then they could surely hear us.

"Scream if you need to," Dov said again, importunate.

Sex with Dov was not a screaming sort of thing. It was brief, urgent, and primal. It was as though he was compelled to do it, and I was a minor player. My satisfaction—even my participation—was not an issue for him. I didn't even have to be there, truthfully. So why this sudden need to make conversation?

"You can scream," he said again.

I burst out laughing.

"What?" He recoiled.

"Sorry, Dov—I guess I'm not the screaming type." I stroked his hairy buttocks, trying to soothe him. He pulled away angrily.

"It's not good for you?" He rolled off me and turned his back.

I had hurt his feelings.

"Come on, Dov, I'm sorry," I said, rubbing his back. Sweat sluiced off him and dripped onto my belly. It reminded me of washing down a horse, using a metal scraper to remove excess moisture.

What was I doing?

"I just—I'm not a screamer."

"And you find this comical?"

"No, I just—I just stepped out of my body for a moment. I—I just—I couldn't take you seriously. I'm sorry," I said.

Did he really think that he was such a great lover that he could provoke screams?

"Come on, Dov, be a sport. Sex is funny sometimes."

"I'm glad you think so. It's good to know this about you."

Ah, the male ego!

"I mean, take you, for example," I said. "Sex with you is like the Kentucky Derby."

Did I really just say that?

"What do you mean?"

"It's the most exciting two and a half minutes of my life."

Dov got up and walked away from the bed, keeping his back to me.

"You can go now."

In Dov's bathroom, brushing my teeth with my finger before the subway ride home, I rummaged idly through his medicine cabinet. I had not bothered to turn on the light. He had stopped speaking to me, but I had more pressing concerns, such as having to come back to work that night on very little sleep.

There was a diaphragm in a little beige case on the second shelf.

I opened the case. It was a size 65. Mine was a 75.

The O.R. nurse, I thought briefly.

I wanted to leave a little note inside the case:

> Hi! How long does he take with
> you? With me he has never exceeded three minutes forty
> seconds. Call me: 212-555-4351.

160

"I can't believe it!" Moe said, when I told her that night.

"Can't believe what?"

"You deliberately, willfully gave up mediocre sex for *no sex at all!*"

"It wasn't mediocre. It was just—fast. Besides, I am not a kid any more. I'd like to actually feel something for the person I'm boinking. I mean, besides an itch that needs to be scratched."

"Oooh, you're so *mature,*" Moe said sarcastically.

The Night of the Three Almontes/*La Noche de las tres Almontes*

It was Saturday night of Labor Day Weekend. Moe and I were starting midwifery school at the New York State University College of Health Sciences (NYSUCHS, or "NYsucks") on Monday. We had been working at NYCAS for more than a year.

I was the charge nurse that night, inexplicably. Although I was a good nurse, it was clear to all my colleagues that I was not a leadership type.

"I'm more of a 'crying in the bathroom' type," I pointed out, urgently lobbying Debbie to take over charge-nurse duty that night.

Debbie would not be moved.

"I took charge Thursday and Friday," she said. "I'm fried."

Being in charge meant delegating; it meant taking a leadership role; it meant giving assignments to your friends and colleagues. It meant arranging lunch breaks, doling out the work fairly. I did not have the requisite self-esteem to do that, so I often wound up doing most of the assignments myself, which invariably led to me crying in the bathroom by the end of the shift.

I had just successfully delegated a STAT c-section to Moe and Debbie. Moe was the scrub nurse and Debbie was the circulator. I had given a dinner break to Wendy; Julie was in a delivery and Laurie and Madeleine were setting up the other O.R. O'Donnell was making coffee. I was alone at the desk. It was 1:40 a.m.

EMS rolled in.

"Got one!" the EMT yelled cheerfully as he pushed the stretcher. The woman on it appeared to be full-term and in no acute distress.

Ah, EMS, the great taxi service for the pregnant! People died of heart attacks waiting for the ambulance to arrive, yet many pregnant women in the neighborhood of NYCAS felt okay about calling the ambulance for just about anything—annoying vaginal discharge, itching, spotting, "pain in my stomach," ruptured membranes, etc. It was as though the pregnancy granted them some special status, or worse—as though they had never previously given any thought to how the pregnancy might wind up—with ruptured membranes, for example, or labor, or a little *bloody show* (blood-tinged, mucousy vaginal discharge) as the contractions got started.

"Nine months, H_2O not broken, lower abdominal cramping. Sign here!"

"Listen, guys," I said. "Get a clue." I was too tired even to stand at that moment, but I had enough energy to be rude. "Stop saying, 'H_2O not broken.' It's not H_2O. It makes you sound ignorant."

"It's not?"

"I mean, I know you want to sound scientific and all that, but it's really not H_2O."

"It's not water?"

"Not, strictly speaking, water. It's water and salts and fetal urine and—"

"Really? The baby makes pee-pee in there? But, why do they call it 'the water' then, if it's not water?"

"I don't know—" I searched for his name tag "—Rudy. It's a—an ancient term. 'The waters' is what it's really called. But it's *not* H_2O!"

"Huh! You live, you learn," Rudy said. "So sign here."

The patient's name was Norma Almonte, and she refused to get off the stretcher. I had not yet arisen from my chair.

"Mrs. Almonte? Do you speak English? My name is Sarah Porter? I'm the nurse in charge? The EMS guys need their stretcher back, so would you mind just climbing down and sitting on that chair right there?" I gestured to the triage area.

"I can't."

"Why not?" I was curious.

"Because the baby is going to come out."

"What makes you say that? You look very comfortable—you haven't even broken a sweat—and—what makes you say that? All I'm asking you to do is move over to that chair there." My feet were throbbing.

"I can't. Because the baby is coming. I had a cerclage."

"Oh, a cerclage!" [A cerclage is a surgical stitch placed in the cervix by an obstetrician in early pregnancy when there is a threat or a history of *incompetent cervix*—where the cervix dilates painlessly in the second trimester and spits out a non-viable baby. The cerclage holds the cervix closed. In late pregnancy, the stitch is taken out.]

"Yep. They took it out this morning. And the baby is going to come out now."

"So you can't get off the stretcher?"

"Nope."

"What if I gave you a little bucket? And you held it under yourself?" I was begging.

"Nope."

Bone-weary, I got up and wheeled Mrs. Almonte into the triage room. I helped her slide over onto the bed. I began to remove her pantyhose. As I did so, a full-term baby girl slid out onto the bed.

Just like that.

"Wow. You were right," I said admiringly.

"GET ME A SET-UP NOW!" I screamed to the unshakable Mrs. O'Donnell, our receptionist. *"AND PAGE DR. CHI!"*

The baby lay on the bed in a puddle of amniotic fluid, thrashing and crying. I had nothing—no cord clamps, no blankets, no drapes, nothing. I couldn't even reach the glove box behind me on the wall.

"Wow. Thank God for panty hose, huh?" I tried to calm Mrs. Almonte with humor. "Are they the control-top kind?"

Rudy stuck his head in the door and beheld Mrs. Almonte's new daughter.

Where was that set-up?

"Wow. Congratulations. Uh, Miss?"

"Yes, Rudy, you can take the stretcher now."

"Uh, Miss? We need the vitals."

"What are you talking about?"

"We need her vital signs? For the report?"

"Rudy. Does it look like I have time to take her vital signs? Would you hand me some gloves, please?"

O'Donnell brought in a delivery table. (Mrs. O'Donnell, our steely, silver-haired Spanish-speaking unit receptionist could, in a pinch, act as de facto nurse's aide or even as nurse. Years of working in L&D at night had prepared her for almost any emergency, and she always knew what to do.)

I clamped the cord, cut it, and gave the baby to Nancy Almonte to hold.

Rudy was persistent.

"We really need the vital signs, Miss."

"110/80, 98.5, 92, 20."

"Thank you, Miss," he said, scribbling franti-cally. "And have a nice night."

"Rudy?"

"Yes, Miss?"

"How about that? A righteous use of the Emergency Medical System!"

3:15 a.m. A teenage girl with a very small bel-ly appeared at the nurses' station with an older woman, probably her mother.

"How may I help you?"

Bilateral Bugs Bunny signs.

"Que paso?" (What happened?)

"Ella tiene nueve meses. Tiene dolor de cabeza muy grave." (She is nine months pregnant. She has a very bad headache.)

"Recibiste cuidado prenatal?" (Did you have pre-natal care?)

"Ella llego de Santo Domingo ayer." (She just ar-rived from Santo Domingo yesterday.)

On the stretcher in the triage room, the little girl—whose name was Teresita Almonte—had a blood pressure of 200/110. It had to be a mistake. I took it again. 190/108.

I screamed to O'Donnell: "Page Dr. Chi again!"

Where was that guy?

He hadn't responded to my page about the first Almonte for almost fifteen minutes. That, at least, did not require medical expertise. This was serious. This was severe preeclampsia. [Preeclampsia, a mysterious, fairly common condition of late pregnancy, features dangerously high blood pressure and sometimes affects kidney and liver function and the ability of the blood to clot. In its worst form, if unchecked, preeclampsia can progress to *eclampsia*, in which the patient experiences uncontrolled seizures.]

I started preparing an IV.

As I pricked her skin with the angiocath, Teresita Almonte began having a full-blown eclamptic seizure. Her head thrashed from side to side, her arms contracted tightly against her chest, her back arched stiffly and her legs kicked out in front of her. She was foaming at the mouth and making a raspy sound. She urinated on herself. Her mother stared passively.

"Jesus!"

I had to get that IV in, *now*.

I pleaded with the girl's mother: "*Ve te a la estacion de las enfermeras. Diganos que hay un problema muy grave aqui. Necesito ayuda ahora mismo!*" (Go to the nurses' station and tell us [okay, my Spanish was not perfect] that there is a very serious problem here. I need help right now!)

She ran off in the wrong direction.

"*A la derecha*!" I screamed (To the right!).

I was terrified. I had never seen an eclamptic seizure before. Where was everybody? Teresita continued thrashing and bucking. I prayed: "Please, God—Jesus—let me get this IV in *now*."

168

I followed the movements of her arm. During a millisecond of stillness, I jabbed the IV angiocath into a vein and saw the reassuring flash of blood. I was in.

O'Donnell appeared in the doorway.

"Everybody's in the O.R. The patient's bleeding. What's the matter?"

"Get me Dr. Chi now! And get the attending in here! Jeez, Louise, she's having a seizure!"

She disappeared. As an afterthought, I yelled, "Bring me the crash cart!"

It took two ampules of Valium to break Teresita Almonte's seizures. Once she was stable, the house attending, Karen Noble, and the second-year resident, Raymond Chi, took her to the O.R. and delivered a healthy but undersized baby boy. Teresita, loaded up with Magnesium sulfate, Valium and phenobarbitol, was transferred to the Recovery Room and had no more seizures.

5:00 a.m.

A woman strolled up to the nurses' station clutching her belly gingerly, as though trying to hold something in.

"What's up?" I asked. Madeleine and I were trying to catch up on the notes from Teresita's admission. Moe was taking a break. Debbie was in a delivery with Dr. Wallace. Raymond was making rounds on the postpartum floor downstairs.

"I'm bleeding too much," she said.

I stood up, leaning over the nurses' station, and stared down her body.

She was bleeding into her socks.

"Maddie," I murmured, trying to get her attention without seeming alarmed. She stood up and looked.

"Jesus fucking Christ!" Maddie clamped her hand over her mouth.

"Sorry!"

The woman was strangely calm.

"It's too much, blood, right? I knew when I saw it that it was too much blood. I didn't have this much blood with my first."

I glanced at O'Donnell, who sat, her hand on the phone, ever vigilant, awaiting further instructions.

"Page the attending? Page Dr. Chi?"

"Yep. Anesthesia also."

Her name was Lillian Almonte. We flung her onto the bed in an unoccupied labor room and peeled off her clothes. Blood ran down her thighs, soaking the sheets. As I removed her panties, a clot the size of a dessert plate gallumphed out onto the mattress.

It was unbearably hot in the room.

As Maddie and I rushed around, starting her IV, checking her blood pressure, we interrogated her frantically, as though we could get an explanation from her history.

"What is your due date?

"Is this your first baby?"

"Do you come to the clinic here?"

"Who's your doctor?"

"Any problems during this pregnancy?"

"Did you have the diabetes test?"

"Shhhhhhh!" Maddie hissed.

We froze. She was trying to hear the fetal heart tones with the monitor.

Nothing.

The monitor was set at maximum volume. Every time Maddie moved it to a new location on Lillian's abdomen, trying to find the fetal heart sounds, it made a crashing sound.

Her belly was rigid. Except for the harsh sounds of the monitor moving on her belly, it was silent inside that uterus.

Raymond had a puzzled look on his face as he moved the sonographic transducer back and forth across Lillian's belly. Minutes went by. No one spoke.

Lillian's bloody clothes lay balled up at the foot of the bed. Maddie had blood on her bare arms, on her face even. Nobody moved.

"What's wrong?" Lillian asked. "Is everything all right? Why am I bleeding?"

Ray didn't answer, just kept sliding the transducer back and forth, looking confused.

"What's wrong? Is something wrong with my baby? Tell me what's wrong!"

Karen Noble, the house attending, finally told her.

The baby was dead.

Lillian had suffered a complete *abruptio placentae*—a condition in which the placenta shears off the uterine wall, either partially or totally, usually the result of high blood pressure or abdominal trauma. *Partial abruption* was fairly common, and it wasn't always diagnosed in advance. If a small piece of the placenta detached itself, the fetus could survive—usually labor progressed rapidly, with suspiciously heavy bleeding.

But *total abruption* was rare and deadly. Even if the fetus survived, often women who had suffered total abruptio placentae went into DIC—*disseminated intravascular coagulation*—a condition in which the body could no longer clot its own blood, leading to life-threatening hemorrhage.

Forty-five minutes later, Lillian Almonte delivered a perfectly formed, full-term stillborn fetus, complete with membranes and placenta, all in one push.

"I've never seen anything like it," Karen said afterwards, washing her arms at the scrub sinks by the O.R. "Blood pressure normal, no evidence of illicit drug use. The only possible explanation is, she remembers being in an elevator yesterday that stopped short between floors. She got a pretty good jounce. Could that do it?"

She wasn't really asking me. Karen was young, fairly inexperienced, just out of residency, and still enthusiastic about Obstetrics.

It was 6:45 a.m.

Part Three

First Delivery

Dear Diary:

Tonight was the third night of my IP (Intrapartum) Clinical rotation, and I finally had a delivery!

Well, sort of.

I should have had the first delivery of the evening, but that bitch Nancy Solomon was there with me and she *stole a patient* right out from under me.

We were being precepted by darling Marjorie, who could make you feel comfortable facing a firing squad, she is *so* nurturing and loving.

Midwifery education is different from nursing and medical education. Whereas medical education is patriarchal, stern, sadistic and inherently punitive and nursing education is just plain humiliating, midwifery education is matriarchal, nurturing and rewarding. Your preceptors love you for choosing this low-paying, misunderstood, altruistic, body-fluid-flinging profession, and their natural instinct is to nurture you. If you give the wrong answer in class, they correct you sweetly. If you make a mistake, they take you somewhere private and inform you in the gentlest possible way. In medical school and residency, they embarrass you right on the elevator. I've seen it a million times.

I was lurking in the triage area in Labor & Delivery at MC Squared (That's Manhattan County Medical Center —MCMC), working the evening shift, from 3 to 11 p.m.

MC Squared was best known for its failure to flip a patient over in the Emergency Room a few years back. The young man was suffering from a small-caliber gunshot wound to the upper back. (This only happened *once*, mind you.)

For reasons that only medical science can explain, the .22-caliber bullet created a *tamponade* inside the entry wound, preventing blood from leaking out. Unfortunately for the guy, it also nicked the *hepatic portal artery*, an Interstate 80 in the Rand-McNally Atlas of blood vessels.

So the guy lay face up on the gurney in the E.R. at MC Squared, semi-conscious, growing increasingly agitated as blood pumped silently into his abdomen, and not one of the geniuses working that night could figure out what was wrong with him.

It was only when the guy finally *coded* that the astute E.R. staff, attempting to roll him onto the backboard for CPR, noted the small bullet wound near the liver. Too late for him! But many skilled medical personnel learned a valuable lesson that night!

After that I always imagined giant red signs posted throughout the E.R. of MC Squared:

"TURN 'EM OVER!"

Anyway, there I was, brand-new midwifery student, in the triage room of L&D, insanely jealous that Nancy S. already had a patient, when in rolled a pregnant lady *ay-ay-ay-ay*ing the house down and ripping her clothes off.

The most remarkable thing about MC Squared's Labor & Delivery unit, to me, was the inexplicable preference by the staff for the Trendelenberg position (maneuvering the stretcher or bed so that the patient's head is lower than her feet) for all laboring women—a practice not employed by any other science-loving medical facility in the universe—and the complete lack of any semblance of modesty preservation. Women typically labored on stretchers upside-down in open hallways buck-naked. My preceptors used to make nightly "gown rounds," clucking in disapproval and covering all the "nakes," as Moe and I called them, with paper sheets and paper gowns. The staff were oblivious; in fact, the presence of the paper sheets really seemed to annoy them.

"Those damned midwives are at it again, covering everyone up!"

In any case, my patient had clearly been to MC Squared before, because she was tearing her clothes off in the hallway as she approached triage.

Pregnant, in labor and ready to get naked and in Trendelenberg! Now *that's* a good sport!

"*¡Caca! ¡Caca!*" she screamed at me. I helped her to a stretcher and ran to fetch Marjorie. Alas! She was in the Delivery Room with Nancy and her patient.

The Labor & Delivery nurses at MC Squared were not regular recipients of Employee of the Month citations. Nary a one of them ever smiled, comforted a patient or offered a kind word. Thus, the women who came to MC Squared to deliver expected nothing.

Midwifery students, on the other hand, had nothing but compassion and love to give, as our physical and diagnostic skills were limited.

Mrs. Caca seemed agitated. I was alone in triage. *What to do?*

"MIZ TRIPP!" I screamed.

Ms. Tripp was the evening charge nurse. A trip she was indeed. Finding her was a nightly challenge, and getting her to shift her enormous frame from pyramidal to vertical was nigh on impossible. Moreover, she didn't mind letting you know how much you were putting her out.

What did move Ms. Tripp was the nightly arrival of the Roti Guy. Each evening around 7:30 p.m., one of the staff of L&D could be heard to shout, "Roti Guy!," whereupon all employees raced to the elevators.

The Roti Guy, a West Indian whose dreadlocks were always covered in an enormous green-red-and-gold ski cap, dispensed chicken, vegetable and beef/?horse? roti from a bread van in the MC Squared parking lot. For a mere $3.50, one could eat like a king every night.

Ms. Tripp had to be with the Roti Guy, because she wasn't responding to my distress calls and the timing was about right.

Min Pao, nurse extraordinaire, loomed in the doorway of triage. Short, squat and with powerful-looking thighs, she resembled nothing so much as the chubby Buddha, but not the smiling one. Min Pao spoke perfectly good English, but it was heavily accented. When conversing with Min Pao, you experienced about a thirty-second brain lag between *her* spoken word and *your* interpretation, with cartoon images popping up in serial fashion to clog your synapses and delay understanding.

To wit:

A handsome, cheerful Indian cardiologist came to L&D to monitor a patient who was having an irregular heartbeat. Min Pao took a liking to this doctor and cleaved to him like a remora to a shark.

When the nice Indian doctor left, Min Pao approached me, of all people, and uttered her first witnessed words of the shift:

"He *nice!* He a *Pharaoh*?"

Cartoon-generated brain cells switched on. I pictured Nice Indian Doctor in full Egyptian headgear making like King Tut. *Pharaoh, Pharaoh, Pharaoh*. Then it came to me:

"Yes, Min Pao! He's the *Cardiology Fellow*!"

Standing in the doorway of Triage, Min now glowered at me.

"How foul she is?"

Foul? Foul? Foul?

"How many shitmitter?"

(Cartoon image: a "shit-meter." *We are talking caca, after all*.)

"Oh! How *far* is she? How many *centimeters*? I don't know, Min Pao, shall I examine her?"

Mrs. Caca looked up at me pleadingly.

"*Ay, ay, ay, ay, ay, ay, ay, Dios Mio, ayudeme!*" (Oh, oh, oh, oh, oh, oh, oh, my God, help me!) (*And help me too, while you're at it. Find me a nurse who gives a shit!*)

Just then Marjorie appeared, a size-16 goddess.

"How are you getting on? Got somebody active?"

"Yeah, I think so. Got a minute?"

With Marjorie's guidance, I determined that Mrs. Caca was eight shitmitters dilated. She was bearing down with every contraction.

Marjorie, ever ready, ran to the other Delivery Room to set up the instrument table.

Min Pao glared at me suspiciously.

"Baby coming! You take to Dee-All?" *(Dee-All?Dee-All?Dee-All? DR? Delivery Room?)*

"Yes, Min Pao, will you join me?"

She grunted disapprovingly.

"I go for paper woks!" She disappeared. (*Paper woks*? Why? Were we having dim sum?)

Mrs. Caca grabbed my scrub top and began to pull herself up from the stretcher.

"Baby coming!" (Her only attempt at English, but it was flawless.)

I grabbed the foot of the stretcher and hauled it through the doorway.

"*MIN PAO!*" I screamed.

No response.

"*¡Caca! ¡Caca! ¡Caca!*" from the stretcher.

I began running down the hall pulling the foot of the stretcher, its head listing wildly to right and left.

"*MIN PAO!*"

As I got to the doorway of the Delivery Room, something told me to re-evaluate the patient's condition. I lifted the sheet. There, between Mrs. Caca's legs with its chin embedded in a little mountain of shit, was a baby's head. It was frantically rotating itself from side to side, trying to complete its delivery, blinking its little eyes and spitting up.

I threw the sheet back over Mrs. Caca and pushed the stretcher toward the delivery table.

"*MIN PAO! THE BABY'S HERE!*"

Marjorie ran past me to the bed, took a look, and began to shake with laughter.

"Just get the baby out, Sarah, for God's sake! Get some gloves on. You don't need Min Pao!"

I bare-handed the baby out of Mrs. Caca, a very bad idea in those days of deadly viruses, but there were no gloves in sight. I had no idea how long the baby had been sitting there eating shit, but it couldn't have been more than a minute.

After I clamped and cut the cord and suctioned the baby's mouth and nose, I held him aloft, displaying all of his triumphant parts for Mrs. Caca's enjoyment.

"*¡Varón!*" I proclaimed (Baby boy!)

I glanced at Marjorie, who had slumped onto a stool. She was still laughing, in that silent, whole-body-shaking way that precedes violent screams.

"*Como se llama?*" (What's his name?)

"*Ellll*-veeeeess," Mrs. Caca said shyly. (*Elvis?*)

And that was my first delivery.

Sharlene

Sharlene was fourteen years old. She was a Para 0020. That meant, in obstetrical talk, that she had been a busy girl.

The four digits in the "Parity" system refer to a woman's lifetime pregnancy history. The first number represents full-term babies delivered, of which Sharlene had had none. The second number stands for premature deliveries—again, none for this girl. The third number represents abortions and miscarriages. She had had two of those. The last number represents living children. She was about to have one, but until she delivered, she was a Para 0020.

"How on earth could she have time to get pregnant *three times*?" Marjorie wondered aloud. "Ask her when she became sexually active and how many partners she's had since becoming sexually active."

"Oh, you mean, like, take a complete sexual history?"

"Yeah, that, and I'm really, really, really curious," Marjorie replied. "Where was her mother? Doesn't she get involved with her kid at all?"

Marjorie had one child, a 13-year-old girl, to whom she had given birth quite late in life, long after she had given up hope. She carried elaborate photo arrays of Maura at all times, and always had a cute-Maura story for anyone with five minutes to spare. It was the only sentimentality that she ever showed. All the sarcasm, all the cyanide-laced humor she displayed about every other aspect of her life—it all disappeared when she talked about Maura. Even when she was diagnosed with the breast cancer that would eventually kill her, she showed no trace of emotion; just a grim determination to survive.

Not that Marjorie wasn't kind and nurturing. She was one of the kindest people I have ever known. But everything she did was conducted without sentimentality, except when it came to her daughter, where she was a complete sucker.

I went into Sharlene's room, pen at the ready, determined to take the most elaborate history ever taken by a midwifery student. There would be no stone unturned. All the mysteries of her fourteen years would be unraveled. She would confide in me, and I would *get the story*. For a moment or two, I felt like a journalist again.

There was a pervasive smell of cooked meat in the room that I could not fathom. It reminded me of my next-door neighbor's outdoor grill very long ago. I closed my eyes for a minute. I could still picture the rusting swingset in their side yard.

Four people gazed up at me from various perches. A young man in a baseball cap with a long stringy ponytail sat on the floor. A woman in her twenties shared an armchair with a slightly older woman. Each had one butt-cheek in the chair and one butt-cheek hanging off the side. An ancient woman with only two visible teeth sat on a small rolling stool. Each was eating voraciously out of White Castle bags.

"Wow," I said admiringly. "White Castles." The smell of it was making me gag—it was only 8:15 a.m.

Sharlene lay on her side in the bed, wearing a white paper gown, snoring. She was a generously proportioned girl, and could easily have been mistaken for sixteen or seventeen. Her limp brownish hair was matted to one side, standing up slightly. As I approached her, she woke up, rolled to the edge of the bed, bit her own index finger and screamed, doubling at the waist.

"ANOTHER ONE!" she yelped. The monitor registered a contraction. She made a low growling noise and thrashed around in the bed, her bracelets clanging into the side railings.

The toothless woman cackled over a mouthful of mini-cheeseburger.

"That'll teach 'er," she said, to no one in particular.

Sharlene opened her eyes and fixated on me.

"You got to help me! Please, Miss!"

"What can I do for you?" I asked cheerily. "Actually, I need to ask you some questions. How old are you?"

"*Not that again!* Please help me, Miss. I need a painkiller, I really do! I'm begging you! That other stuff didn't work, I swear!" She grabbed my scrub top and twisted it, pulling me closer. She had extraordinary upper body strength. I was almost on top of the bed.

The family continued to make sucking and smacking noises, oblivious. The girl and I were nose to nose. Her breath had that acetone sweetness of someone who has not eaten in a very long while—metallic, overwhelming, yet sugary, like artificially flavored peaches.

The nurse stalked in. Sharlene eyeballed me one last time, released her grip and rolled onto her side, sighing. A racking snore shook the bed, causing the metal railings to hum.

"What are you doing?" the nurse addressed the family members. "You can't eat in here!"

"What do you mean, Miss? We're hungry!" the ancient one implored her.

"You'll have to go out to the waiting room with that," the nurse insisted.

Reluctantly they stashed their nutrients in their original bags and left.

"I mean, *really*! Did you get a load of that?" The nurse rolled her eyes in my direction.

Sharlene, who had fallen silent, again awoke and reached for me.

"Please, Miss! You gotta help me!"

"Why is she so sleepy?" I asked the nurse.

"She got Stadol a while back," the nurse said. Stadol is a synthetic narcotic, generally given "IV push"—injected directly into the intravenous tubing and "pushed" into the patient's bloodstream by dripping the IV fluid rapidly behind it. Its primary effect on laboring women seemed to be to make them sleep soundly between contractions, becoming extremely agitated—but still drowsy —when a contraction disturbed their sleep.

Before I could reply, Sharlene drifted off again.

I wondered what to do. Should I crawl back to Marjorie, dejected, and admit that the patient was too drugged to give me the skinny on her sex life? Or should I stay and wake her up and try to badger her into giving up the info? She was my patient, after all; with any luck I'd be delivering her baby. I needed to know everything about her.

"She doesn't know who the father is, you know."

I spun around. The tiny ancient woman had reappeared in the doorway.

"I beg your pardon?"

"She doesn't know who the father is." She reached into a fold in her sweat pants and produced a tiny box of raisins.

Two bony fingers scraped the inside of the box, fishing out a raisin.

"She claims it was two guys from her school. She went to a party. I told her mother she was too young to hang out with them worthless people, but she never pays me any mind."

"You mean she was raped?"

"Naw. She just drank too much beer, that's all, and got herself in a tight spot."

"That sounds like rape to me."

"We're keeping the baby, though. She's gonna give it to me and her auntie to raise."

"Why can't she and her mother raise the baby?"

"Her mother don't want no part of it. Got her own fish to fry. Can't barely take care of this one here," the old lady said, gesturing to the poor girl in the bed. "She'll be moving back to Maryland soon."

"How old are you, ma'am?"

"Me? I'll be fifty-two next November."

I almost gasped out loud. She looked to be at least seventy. How did she lose all her teeth?

Sharlene reawakened at that moment.

"*PLEASE, MISS!* Do something! I got to doo-doo!"

This was an unexpected development. The urge to doo-doo usually meant that it was time to push, that the patient was *fully dilated*, ready to enter *the second stage of labor*. Could I be that lucky? The girl had been only three centimeters dilated an hour ago.

Sure enough, Marjorie confirmed my vaginal exam: Fully dilated and ready to push.

"God always takes care of teen mommies," Marjorie said solemnly. It was true; they did seem to have the fastest labors.

The family drifted back into the room. Sharlene was still groggy, just enough to be uncooperative, but agitated enough to resist our efforts to help.

She screamed, "Please, Miss! You got to give me something! A painkiller, something! *Anything!* I got to doo-doo *NOWWWWW!*"

Between bargaining for painkillers, she'd contort, twisting to the side, and bear down, making hacking and growling sounds while kicking her legs out in front of her.

I tried to encourage her to adopt a more physiologically sound position, such as squatting, lying on her side holding her upper leg up, or lying on her back with her legs held up by her "support persons." She would have no part of it.

After about fifteen minutes, Marjorie pulled me aside.

"Just leave her alone," she whispered. "She'll push it out."

I sat on a stool and watched as the little girl twisted, contorted, screamed, cursed and grunted with increasing urgency as the baby's head descended. It was almost impossible to monitor the fetus, because Sharlene was so agitated that she couldn't stay in any position for long. After awhile the nurse gave up and made me hand-hold the monitor against her belly between pushes.

During one of these moments, as I repositioned the monitor against her belly to try to hear the baby's heart rate, the young man got up suddenly and approached me.

"Miss, you got a menu or something?"

"Huh?"

"You got a Chinese menu?"

"Who are you?"

"I'm her cousin."

"You got a name?"

"Albert."

"Well, Albert, I'm a little busy here. Why don't you find something useful to do, like giving her some support? Why are you asking for a menu anyway?"

"Her mother's hungry, Miss."

"Hungry? *What is wrong with you guys?* Why can't you help her?" I realized I was a little out of line, but *really*! A Chinese menu!

Albert was stricken.

"What you want me to do, Miss?"

"Help me hold her legs up. Talk to her. Encourage her."

"Sharlene, listen to the lady, please," Albert addressed her.

God really does look after teen mommies. Soon we were seeing the baby's head every time she pushed.

Albert began to shout syllables of encouragement in a loud, hoarse voice.

"Come on! I see it! Go! Go! Go! Go!"

"Come on, Sharlene," I finally said. "Don't you want this over with?"

"Try a modified Ritgen," Marjorie whispered in my ear as I struggled to deliver the baby's head. Sharlene seemed to be sucking the head back after every push, as though she was afraid to deliver it, and she kept scooching up the bed so that I was almost climbing onto the bed after her.

The *modified Ritgen maneuver* involves placing a sterile towel over your hand and then "milking" the baby's chin up through the patient's rectum, using only *external massage of the perineum* (the muscle and skin between the vagina and rectum)

It seemed to be working.

All at once the draped, muffled shape of Sharlene rose up in the bed like a restless spirit. The high-intensity light over the bed reflected off her hair, which had a strange, white-hot appearance.

There was complete silence for a moment; then:

"Do somebody have they finger in my dookey-hole?"

It seemed pointless to pretend otherwise.

"That's correct!"

"Well, *get it out*!"

The baby delivered in a perfect arc. In real life, unlike TV and movies, the deliverer doesn't stand directly in front of the patient, but slightly to the side, facing the same way the baby's head will eventually face. After the baby's head delivers, after you have suctioned the nose and mouth with a bulb syringe and felt around the baby's neck to make sure there is no loop of cord there, the baby will wisely begin to rotate its head slightly. It does this to realign itself with its shoulders inside, which are at an oblique angle in the mother's pelvis. Then the entire head rotates to the side, telling you that the shoulders inside have also rotated. So if the baby is eyeballing the door, that's the way you stand also. If the baby is looking towards the windows, you shift your body to face the window also.

In our cramped, overheated midwifery classroom, we had once rehearsed the so-called *cardinal movements of labor* as a group, each of us playing the part of the fetus. Dutifully we stood beside our desks in a circle, each holding a fetus-size doll and stuffed cloth pelvis. As our instructor intoned the names of the various movements—Engagement, Descent, Flexion, and so on—we had each manipulated our little fetus's head and body through its life-size female pelvis. In this way we could better understand and visualize the maneuvers the brave little fetus must make to be born.

Delivering a baby is not so much pulling it out as bending it down and back up again. There's a shelf of bone above it (the mother's *symphysis pubis*) and a bowl-shaped bone below (the *sacrum* and *coccyx* of the posterior pelvis), and its two little shoulders are wedged between those two bones. So you wiggle the baby downward to release the upper shoulder from behind the symphysis pubis, and then wiggle it upward to release the lower shoulder from the bowl of the sacrum and coccyx. Done properly, a baby should wiggle down, up and then in a round curve onto the mother's belly quite naturally.

This is what I did with Sharlene's baby. It's a handy place to rest the baby for a minute, the mother's belly, so you can suction and inspect the baby with no fear of dropping it. Before I could catch my breath, examine the baby's genitalia, and inform her of what she had won, Sharlene's voice rose up from beneath the paper drapes:

"Get that shit off me!"

I grabbed the baby back and yanked it to my chest protectively.

Marjorie gasped. I looked over at her. Her eyes, above her mask, welled up.

"It's a girl," I said weakly.

"Well, good!" the patient's mother finally addressed Sharlene. "I hope some day she puts you through this exact same mess!"

And that was my tenth delivery.

The Four P's

In one of our first lectures in midwifery school, we learned about the Four Ps, which are the very essence of labor and delivery.

The first P stands for the Psyche. A woman's attitude has a lot to do with how she will labor, believe it or not. Fear, dread, post-traumatic stress, domestic violence, childhood abuse, the expectation of loss of control and/or loss of status—all of these come into play when you're in labor.

Some women just can't go into labor, period. These are the women who come for a check-up at 41 1/2 weeks, swollen, crying, exhausted, frustrated, sick of being pregnant. They end up getting induced. It's a nightmare.

It's about *control*, people. If you think that you can control what happens to you when you have a baby, you will be bitterly disappointed. All during your pregnancy, you must repeat to yourself until you believe it:

I have no control over what is about to happen to me. The only thing I can control is how I respond to it.

So-called childbirth education can have a great influence on the laboring woman's psyche, actually. Some childbirth educators preach that a *natural* labor is better, safer, and so on, suggesting that all drugs and "interventions" in labor are dangerous, the invention of the devil, etcetera. They are, in a sense, giving pregnant women permission to believe they can actually control the whole thing—design it, orchestrate it, conduct it, creating the perfect, *natural* labor for themselves. As though *planning* will make it so.

If I make a "birth plan" that allows for no medications or interventions, then I won't need any!

Midwives in these times are stuck between the rock of childbirth education and the hard place of modern obstetrics. We encourage our patients to go to childbirth education classes, yes, because it gives them a sense of control and power. But if the labor goes sour and the woman needs an obstetrical-type intervention, such as Pitocin, she has now been exquisitely trained to reject such interventions as diabolical attempts to take away her control and render her helpless. Then the midwife becomes the bad guy, after months of being the benign, trustworthy, woman-friendly, feminist good guy.

It's like date rape, from the patient's point of view. You met the guy in your sociology seminar, he seemed nice, you had coffee a couple of times, and now suddenly he's on top of you, holding your arms against your sides, breathing his hot, beery breath in your face.

But we *are* the good guys. I went into this profession so that I could give control back to women, not so that I could control them. So if I, the good guy, say, *I'm very sorry, but this labor needs some Pitocin*, is it appropriate for the patient to get out her pepper spray?

Is *natural* labor better?

First of all, there's that word. *Natural.*

Meaning that anything other than a completely spontaneous, unmedicated delivery is *unnatural.*

Secondly, there's a mistaken belief among the lay population that any *vaginal* birth is "natural."

There's *"natural "*—no medication, no interventions by the obstetrician or midwife to affect the course of the labor, nothing artificial at all. But the word carries enormous judgment.

There's *vaginal*—which can occur with or without forceps or a vacuum/suction device, with or without an epidural, with or without narcotic pain relief, with or without a huge episiotomy, with or without lying flat on your back with or without your feet in stirrups. Not quite *natural*. But definitely through the vagina.

But telling a woman in advance of labor that it's *always better and safer* to go through it without any pain relief or "interventions"—as if all such interventions were equally evil—clearly implies that it's *less good, less safe,* to accept interventions or take pain relief if it's offered.

And that implies that someone else knows better than the woman herself what is good for her.

What makes a "natural" labor better?

Do the drugs and interventions we offer women in labor—to make them comfortable, or to improve the quality of the labor, or to avoid a cesarean delivery—cause harm?

Most narcotics clear the woman's system quickly, within a matter of hours, and are out of the baby's system a while later. The narcotics and anesthetics used in an epidural don't even touch the baby, since there's very little uptake of the medications into the woman's circulation. The epidural meds hang out in the narrow, enclosed space overlying the spinal cord, blunting the pain response as it goes to the brain. So the woman knows she's having a contraction, but it doesn't bother her.

Natural?

No.

Diabolical?

Naw.

Pitocin (the synthetic hormone used to induce or jump-start labor), while clearly artificial, if used correctly and for good reasons, emulates and enhances the body's own labor-causing substances, usually resulting in *progressive labor.*

Does anybody have a problem with that?

Unnatural?

It is decidedly so.

Unsafe?

Is it better, safer and more natural for a woman who has been in labor at home for 15 hours, vomiting for the last three, who faces another eight to ten hours of labor, to refuse all interventions designed to correct dehydration and *ketosis* (a potentially harmful condition brought on by starvation and/or vomiting)? Is it better to refuse interventions that may cause efficient contractions that may, in turn, achieve cervical dilation and allow the woman to relax sufficiently that the fetus' head will descend into the pelvis, making it easier for her to push?

Maybe not.

Does being a modern midwife mean that I, Sarah Porter, have to espouse a militant, rigid stance? Do I believe that all medications, all interventions, are equally and inherently evil and will detract from the woman's "experience" of labor?

Hell, no.

My job is to deliver the baby safely. Since I cannot perform a cesarean section, I must try my best to deliver the baby vaginally. If it appears obvious that a cesarean section is the best way for the baby to be born, my job is to inform the woman and then calmly make arrangements. But since my primary goal is a safe vaginal delivery, if I believe that an "intervention" will accomplish that, it is my duty to share my expertise with my patient, suggesting and then performing said intervention.

Of course, I didn't know this yet when I first heard about the Four Ps.

The second P stands for the Passage. The passage is the pelvis. Most women have a nice round passage—the *gynecoid pelvis*—that will allow an average-size fetus to pass through without too much argument.

Some other, unfortunate women have a male-type pelvis—the *android pelvis*—that is funnel-shaped, tight, heavy-boned and resistant to the passage of anything through it.

And some equally unfortunate women have a flat pelvis—the *platypelloid pelvis*—that will not allow a round-headed fetus to pass through.

And still other women have an *anthropoid pelvis*—roomy in the back, tight in the front—that will usually permit passage of a fetus after lots of drama and misery.

Variations on these four pelvic types include the *ATR pelvis* —"admits truck readily"—through which a two-year-old could fit, and the *hellno* pelvis—difficult to characterize, but you know nothing's going to pass through it, ever.

If the pelvis is willing, the labor may progress well, the fetus may descend, and the delivery may be accomplished vaginally.

Moe and I and two other midwifery school classmates, Terry and Suzanne, learned the fine art of pelvic evaluation, speculum placement and *bimanual exam* in Moe's apartment one Thursday night after class. (A bimanual exam entails placing two fingers in the patient's vagina to feel the contour and shape of the cervix and pelvis while simultaneously palpating the patients' lower abdomen—to feel the ovaries and uterus—with the other hand.) The deal was, until we had practiced sufficiently on each other in our classroom/lab, we would not be allowed to examine real patients.

"This is the easiest and best way to learn proper exam technique," our instructor explained. "By examining each other, you can get feedback about what hurts and what doesn't, and which techniques are most effective and comfortable."

Moe had the bright idea of doing the "lab" in her apartment.

"Can we practice in our own homes and then come back to school to be evaluated?" she asked Harriet, the faculty coordinator of the "Well-Woman Gynecology, Part I" module.

Harriet couldn't see why not.

As F.I.N.A. founders, Moe and I believed in self-medicating, where appropriate, before undertaking challenging assignments (not those involving patient care, of course).

Before we knew it, ice, vodka, orange juice and grenadine were pureeing in the blender, Bruce Springsteen was on the stereo and we were assembling our instruments. This was much better than the cold, impersonal lab, with its torn-up vinyl exam tables and harsh fluorescent lighting.

"Your pelvis is really roomy, Maureen," Suzanne murmured enthusiastically as she poked

Moe's coccyx up and down while Terry and I watched. Moe languished on her fake-velvet sofa, her butt elevated on two cushions.

"Hold on a sec," Moe said into the phone. She draped her palm over the receiver as Suzanne continued walking around in her bones.

"It's my Irish heritage," she whispered. "We have big pelvises as a rule. It's a survival thing."

"My ancestors toiled in the potato fields, giving it up to their husbands every couple of rows," she elaborated. "They'd just bend over and … boom! There he'd be, doing his husband thing. Then, nine months later out would drop a rug rat in those same furrows."

She removed her hand from the receiver and continued, "Yeah, Mom, I'm fine. Yeah, it's going pretty well."

That was the second P.

In labor, a lot depends on the third P – the Powers. The Powers are the *contractile forces generated by the uterus.*

If a woman's Powers are *inadequate,* she is likely to receive the Sixth P: Pitocin.

Pitocin is the synthetic form of the naturally-occurring hormone, oxytocin, that is released by your pituitary gland when you are in labor.

Pitocin is given for just about anything these days. But if a woman's Powers are doing the job, she shouldn't need the Sixth P.

There is a belief held by many lay people, which is routinely passed on to pregnant women:

Labor with Pitocin is worse than "regular labor."

Pitocin contractions *hurt more* than regular contractions.

The use of Pitocin may lead to a c-section.

Doctors use Pitocin because they don't possess the Fifth P, which is Patience.

Pitocin is evil, diabolical, the very smegma of Satan, invented for no purpose but to cause women pain.

Do I, Sarah Porter, believe any of the above?

Let's say you're in labor, and you're not progressing past four or five centimeters. Your evil, diabolical, impatient, woman-hating doctor/midwife suggests Pitocin.

Once you are on Pitocin, your contractions *hurt much more* than the ones you had before.

Is it because Pitocin is Satanic, or is it because the contractions you had before were *not strong enough to achieve progress in labor*?

If the latter is true, then of course, the contractions you will have on Pitocin will hurt like hell. Those *nice ones* you had before that *didn't hurt very much* also *didn't do very much*.

Meanwhile the scores of women whose Powers are perfectly adequate, who don't need Pitocin, can tell you that those "natural" contractions that get you to ten centimeters dilated and allow you to push out a baby suck just as bad as the ones induced by Pitocin.

But let's move on to the Fourth P: the Passenger.

If the Passenger is not well at any time during the labor, and if delivery cannot be accomplished shortly after the Passenger declares himself unwell, the baby must be delivered *abdominally* (via c-section).

Does normal labor stress out fetuses?

Not usually. A robust, full-term, average-weight fetus of a well-nourished, healthy mother will not often experience distress related to labor alone. This is because a well-nourished mother without preexisting or pregnancy-induced disease will usually make a placenta—the so-called afterbirth—that weighs close to one kilogram, is fat and spongy and resilient, and is attached to a thick, healthy, umbilical cord. If the placenta is fat and healthy and resilient, and the cord is fat and protected from crushing and compression and damage, the baby fed by the placenta will likewise be fat and spongy and resistant to injury.

If, however, the Passenger, placenta or cord are small, weak or vulnerable to injury, then labor alone may create sufficient stress to necessitate a cesarean delivery.

How do we know this?

Despite all the advances of sonography, biochemistry, and so on, many things in obstetrics remain shrouded in mystery.

What makes labor begin, for example, and what causes preeclampsia, and why some full-term fetuses weigh nine pounds and some weigh five pounds, and why some women can spit out nine-pound babies while bending over their ovens and others struggle to deliver teeny ones, even with apparently good "passages."

One thing that is not mysterious, however, is a "good" fetus.

We infer the status of a fetus in labor by reading the heart-rate pattern generated by it. Healthy fetuses have a classic heart-rate pattern: lots of "variability"—changes in the baseline heart rate within the normal range, and accelerations in the heart rate in response to certain stimuli. Healthy fetuses also move during labor.

A good, well-nourished baby with a big, fat, spongy placenta does not go bad in labor, unless something catastrophic occurs, such as a complete *abruptio placentae* or a cord accident. A cord accident is what happens when the umbilical cord is not protected—say, the level of amniotic fluid is severely diminished—and gets crushed by the weight of the baby, causing asphyxiation.

A good baby does not go bad in labor. This is what Marjorie told us at the beginning of our Intrapartum rotation. This was our mantra, and this was what made it possible to go to work every day.

A good baby does not go bad in labor. Say it with me.

The Fashion Committee of the American Nurse-Midwives Association

It must be asked, and it must be asked outright, without sparing feelings:

Why do so many midwives dress so badly?

This question plagues those few among us who lay claim to this profession and who 've been blessed with something of a fashion sense. When I was attending midwifery school, there seemed to be two basic types of midwives: 1) the hip/hippie, feminist type, and 2) the badly-dressed, self-effacing type.

"Pink polyester blouse—Peter Pan collar—gray polyester midi-skirt, and, whoa—look out!—Birkenstocks with *tube socks*!"

Moe and I were lounging in the lobby of the Desert Hyatt Regency in Palm Springs, waiting for our room to be ready. It was June, and our first American Nurse-Midwives Association (ANMA) annual convention. Midwifery school was all but over. We had aced our Comprehensive Exams, and our State Board exams loomed like a giant turd in the road ahead. We even had jobs lined up—at a hospital in Brooklyn where, in a year's time, we would become part of a private practice if we survived.

We had come for the spa, mainly.

"Could she be ... is it possible ... could she be *a midwife*?"

"Check this one out—long striped shorts, black ankle socks, penny loafers... wait ...wait.... what's that up top? A madras sleeveless shirt! With just a touch of the Kathleen Turner thing! A midwife, perhaps?"

"What's the Kathleen Turner thing?"

"Remember, at the Oscars years ago, when Kathleen Turner accepted the award and she was wearing a sleeveless dress that was much too tight? And those underarm thingies were pouffing out over the edges of the armholes?"

"You're right, it's a bad one," I said, sinking into the worn velvet chair. "Here comes another one!"

The *Bishop score* is an obstetrical method of rating the cervix to determine its "inducibility." If you have to induce someone's labor for some reason, and you want to anticipate your chances of a "successful" induction leading to a vaginal delivery, you can rate the cervix by evaluating its *position* (anterior, posterior or mid-position), softness, *effacement* (how thinned-out it is), *dilatation* (how many centimeters dilated it is), and *station of the head* (how high up or low down in the pelvis the baby's head is). The softer, thinner, more dilated, more *anterior* the cervix, especially when the baby's head is low in the pelvis, the higher the Bishop score and the greater the chance for a successful vaginal delivery.

There in the lobby of the Hyatt, waiting for our room, Moe and I developed a "Fashion score" for midwives everywhere.

With the "Fashion score," you got extra points for choosing completely synthetic fabrics, for always wearing a fanny-pack no matter how formal the occasion, and for sporting items with variants of the word "VAGINA" or "VULVA" on them, such as stunning plastic briefcases and canvas tote bags, given away at midwifery and gynecology conventions by manufacturers of things for the vagina and vulva (in case you were wondering how to get them for yourselves).

The highest-scoring hairdos were those featuring braids (single or double) or Little Dutch Boy bangs. The highest-scoring shoes were, of course, Birkenstocks, but open-toed sandals with socks earned some big points as well. You got bonus points for wearing your ANMA badge well outside the convention hall— such as at an outlet mall 35 miles away—or for wearing knee-high nylons with either Birkenstocks or bright-white

Reeboks. Blouses that racked up major points included polyester gray "satin" ones with built-in ascots, starched pink polyester shirts with stand-up neck ruffles, and white polyester short-sleeved shirts with Peter Pan collars.

High scorers tended to carry canvas bags with inspirational quotations on them, such as "Midwives—Caring for Women," or "The Science of Midwifery, the Art of Caring."

Moe and I had our own versions: "Midwives: The Science of Synthetics, the Art of Bad Shoes." "Midwife Means ... Without Fashion Sense." "Midwives: The Glamour Don'ts."

In these fashion-conscious times, one had to wonder about the whole Fashion Score thing. Do women who choose poorly paying, self-effacing professions make otherwise self-effacing life choices? Was that why so many midwives were overweight and had no recognizable hairstyles? Do most teachers, because they are underpaid and under-respected, dress badly and let themselves go as well? Do overweight, badly dressed women tend to *become* midwives, or do women who are midwives tend to become overweight and badly dressed? Which came first, the tube sock or the Birkenstock?

Were Moe and I and our midwife friends aberrations—dressing decently, getting laid, minding our diets and doing 100 crunches every three days? Could it be that midwives would dress better if they could only afford to? Hadn't they heard of Daffy's and Target and Century 21?

Ironically, I did not yet view midwifery as self-effacing. Poorly paying, for sure, but self-effacing?

Hell, no.

I was going to give women choices; I was going to give them power and control. And I also planned to get a lot of ego strokes and satisfy a lot of neurotic urges in socially acceptable ways by being a midwife.

What if, for example, my excessive need to *nurture* was turned loose on the men in my life? They'd run screaming. They'd leave skid marks. Instead, I would get to act out those impulses on my patients, who would generally appreciate it. Let's face it: When you're in labor, you could use a mommy. I liked being a mommy.

And what about my slavish need to be loved and needed? Whereas most of the men I knew found that quality in me repellent, many of the patients I had encountered in both my nursing career and my midwifery studies truly *did* need and love me. And all I had to do to engender this liking and need was to be kind and compassionate, take good care of them and demonstrate my competence. Once again, a no-lose situation.

Not that everyone has to dress fashionably all the time—not that *we* did, really—but what does it mean when so many midwives look as though they just stepped out of a trailer park after a polyester tornado? Could Moe and I buck this trend? Could we, indeed, establish a "Fashion Committee

Sally Urang

of the American Nurse-Midwifery Association"
and set a firm but fair dress code? Or were we
destined, in the end, to give in, shop for shapeless shifts on sale, buy white tube socks by the
bundle for dress-up, and cut each other's hair to
save money?

I wanted to stand up in the middle of the convention hall and shout:

"Midwives! We have a great job! We're taking
care of *women*! Let's dress better! Let's show our
pride, and honor this great privilege by *turning on
the hall light* before we pick out our clothes in the
morning! Let's *get a professional haircut* once in a
while! Let's use antiperspirant! And let's *throw our
socks out* once we can see our heels through them!
All together now: *NO MORE FANNY PACKS! NO
MORE FANNY PACKS!*"

Maybe not.

Part Four

Delivery Note

The Heights Medical Center, Labor & Delivery, 4/5/99, 8:15 p.m:

Pt arrived to L&D in active labor, had rapid progress to FD [full dilatation] and delivered a liveborn male, Apgar 8/9 [the Apgar score is an immediate eyeball evaluation of the baby's condition, 10 being the highest possible score], wt 4200 gms/9 lbs 4 oz over midline episiotomy. Loose cord around neck easily slipped over head. Bulb suctioned and handed to nurse. Placenta spontaneous/complete with three vessel cord. Fundus [muscular portion of uterus that must contract after delivery to avoid hemorrhage] firm, minimal lochia [the blood expelled by the uterus after delivery]. Repair accomplished using 3.0 and 2.0 ccg under local anesthesia. Good hemostasis achieved. EBL [estimated blood loss{ 450 ccs. Dr. Granville present throughout delivery.

[The patient was admitted at 8 centimeters making a Tarzan-like sound and was immediately put into a birthing room. The patient crawled up the bed on all fours with her buttocks at the head of the bed and her head at the foot of the bed. She would not allow anyone to examine her again, but she began passing stool approximately seven minutes after admission.

Dr. Granville, the house attending, appeared in the doorway as I was putting on my gown and gloves.

"Why isn't she in lithotomy?"

> **Lithotomy** (lî-thot´o-me): incision of a duct or organ for removal of *calculi*.
> **l. position**, the patient lies on his back, legs flexed on the thighs, thighs flexed on the abdomen and *abducted* [held away from the body]. Stirrups may be used to support the feet and legs.

"Lithotomy," from the Greek, means, literally, to cut a stone (*litho* – "stone," *tome* – "to cut"). Developed in 1721, it was first favored for men, to allow a surgeon to incise the urinary bladder to remove a stone, or *calculus*.

Because it renders the patient completely helpless and utterly vulnerable, its value for female patients was soon recognized. Before long, otherwise robust women with no medical condition other than pregnancy were routinely put flat on their backs, legs in stirrups, when delivery was imminent. This position gave the physician total control and rendered the patient helpless, a relationship that has come to characterize modern obstetrics.

Numerous scientific studies have evaluated the efficacy of lithotomy position for delivery, and none to date has found a physiologic advantage to it.

Because the woman is flat on her back, her large blood vessels—which transport blood to her vital organs and placenta—are compressed by the weight of the uterus, effectively cutting off circulation to her brain, heart and lungs—not to mention the placenta. The fetus enters a temporary state of oxygen deprivation and reduced blood flow. The woman, depending on her sensitivity to decreased circulation to her vital organs, may feel weak and lightheaded. Or maybe she just feels helpless. Or maybe she feels really, really angry. And helpless.

But lithotomy is good for us, the deliverers. We can see everything, anatomically speaking. We can completely control the patient's activity, which is, of course, diminished because of the lithotomy position. Best of all, we can even sit on a stool to rest between delivery maneuvers: After all, delivery can be exhausting for the practitioner!

Dr. Granville, who had recently enjoyed a cup of strong coffee and a cigarette, stood next to me, in my personal space, breathing his breath like the flames of hell onto the side of my neck.

"Put her on her back! This is ridiculous! You cannot conduct the delivery safely this way!"

"Dr. Granville, I weigh 128 pounds. Unless she were on fire, I don't think I could wrestle her to the ground. Do you want to try repositioning her? How's your Arabic?"

Dr. Granville glared at me. It was *my* fault, after all, that the patient only spoke Arabic and preferred to have her butt where her head ought to be.

The patient continued to buck and wheel around in the bed like a rodeo bronc, still on all fours. Occasionally she pushed out little turds, which the nurse thoughtfully scooped up in a gauze pad and removed.

"How big is the baby?"

"Dr. Granville, I explained to you already that the patient won't allow anyone to examine her. I just barely got my hands on her belly before she turned over. I think it's about eight pounds, but I didn't really have a chance to do a proper estimate."

"How big were her other kids?"

The stale, acidic odor of the coffee and cigs was making me gag. I turned away as he was speaking and held my gloved hand near my nose and mouth.

"As I already made clear, I don't speak Arabic. If you'd care to inquire about her obstetrical history, I'd appreciate any information you can get."

"Where's her prenatal chart?"

"Her chart has been called for."

The patient pushed forcefully. I saw fetal hair at the *introitus* [vaginal opening]. She had stopped growling and was now, apparently, *pushing effectively.*

"You can't conduct the delivery in this position!"

"Dr. Granville, why not just make the best of it? You know, the all-fours position has been studied in many scientific journals and found to be the best position for delivering a large baby."

"Where did you read that?"

"Dr. Granville, I need to concentrate now."

As the baby's head began to emerge, he grabbed the scissors off the sterile instrument table *with his bare hands.*

"Dr. Granville, what are you doing?"

"At least cut an episiotomy!"

"Are you out of your mind?"

"Get out of my way!" Dr. Granville pushed me aside and cut the patient's perineum. *Without anesthesia.* She howled and swung her head around towards him, as an animal does when wounded. I thought she would attack him, but another contraction overtook her and she began to push.

"Now deliver the baby!"

"Why don't *you* do it, Dr. Granville?"

"Are you refusing?"

"Just get out of the way, please."

I caught the baby's head as it emerged, slipped off the loose loop of umbilical cord around its neck, and suctioned the baby's nose and mouth. With the next contraction, the shoulders delivered in one monstrous push. The baby practically hit me in the chest.]

The Beeper

The first time it goes off, it is 12:04 a.m. I have just completed a couple of REM cycles and I am so deeply asleep I have to swim upwards, to the surface, to figure out what the noise is.

The answering service has renamed my patient, Julianne M.

> *Pls call Jolene M. 9 mos. preg and she*
> *brought her water. 718-555-1987*

Julianne's voice is calm, but there is an edge to it. It is her first baby. Julianne did not, in fact, "bring her water," but "broke" it. She describes clear fluid, says the baby is moving and admits to having irregular crampy sensations in her lower abdomen. I reassure her that these are normal occurrences, and advise her to get some rest for the next few hours, to see if labor begins on its own.

It is then that I begin bargaining with God:

> *Please, just give me until 5 a.m.*

When bargaining with God, I use the same technique as a union representative negotiating a collective-bargaining agreement. I ask for more than I think I'll get.

I lie stiffly in bed for twenty minutes wondering why I can't get back to sleep and what will happen in the next couple of hours. I go over Julianne's pregnancy history in my mind: She's the petite, pretty woman with the tall, gorgeous husband. She works as a high school guidance counselor in Bedford-Stuyvesant. She has a tiny little belly—no more than six pounds, I suspect. She took childbirth classes. She is motivated. She doesn't seem to blame other people for her troubles. I really like Julianne, and what is more, I sort of knew I would end up delivering her. I get these strange voices sometimes. More on this later.

At 3:15 the beeper goes off again. I have been asleep for possibly 45 minutes—a delicious, syrupy, heavy-limbed sleep, the kind that feels like sex.

> *Pls call Seth M. His wife Jolene in labor.*
> *718-555-1987*

Seth says Julianne is in the bathroom on the toilet. He says she's ready to come to the hospital. I remind him that this is Julianne's first baby and that she's only been in labor for a couple of hours. I ask to speak to Julianne.

A long pause, some unidentifiable noises, then the muffled sound of Seth talking to Julianne.

Low mooing sounds, some panting. Then Julianne's voice, different from the one I heard a few hours ago.

I try to get her to talk. This is so I can evaluate the quality of her voice. It's pretty much of a sure thing, when it's a first baby and the woman's voice *between contractions* sounds just like her regular telephone voice or her I've-just-got-a-couple-of-questions voice, that she's not yet in active labor.

Otherwise this whole business of telephone triage is a roll of the dice. Second babies don't waste too much time; first babies take forever.

Usually.

Julianne and I decide that it would be appropriate to meet at the hospital by 4:00 a.m. There is a catch in her voice that impresses me.

Women who are about to have a baby wonder why they shouldn't come to the hospital immediately when they begin contracting. This is the reason:

There is no treatment for early labor. There is no cure for early labor.

It is supposed to happen.

Essentially, in a low-risk pregnancy, once you are in labor there are only two reasons to come to the hospital:

1) you need pain relief;
2) the baby's coming.

Labor, at term, being a normal, expected event, does not require immediate hospitalization. It is *supposed* to happen, it is *good* that it is happening, and there is really nothing to be done about it. There is certainly no need for the drama that we typically see.

"My wife's in a lot of pain!" a man screams at Colleen, the Triage nurse, as though it's her fault. This is after she has explained that the Triage area is full and there will be a brief wait for his wife to be evaluated.

Is Colleen cruel and sadistic to make the man and his wife wait ten minutes?

Hell, no.

What's the big rush, anyway? Labor—at least, the first time around—is all about killing time.

Why not have most of your labor at home, in familiar surroundings, where you are comfortable, can wear your own clothes, can eat and drink freely, and no one is doing things to you? And then come in to the hospital when you're ready to deliver? Or at least when you've gotten past the very early stages.

Because contemporary society has turned labor into an illness, a pathology, a disease, and delivery has become a surgical procedure instead of a normal physiologic event. And there is a widely held belief that modern women should not experience *any pain whatsoever.*

What are we going to do for you at the hospital?

We will start an IV ("as a precaution").

We will give you pain medication ("to help you relax," or because you asked for it).

The combination of these two things is usually sufficient to completely kill the labor, unless it is far advanced.

Oops!

We killed your labor.

Sorry!

So then we have to do something to *correct the reversal of the normal* that we have effected with IV fluid and pain medication.

That means Pitocin, probably.

So let's get this straight.

You're at term, and you're in labor. We give you IV fluid and pain medication, and now you are no longer in labor, so we have to get out the big guns to put you *back into labor*. The reason you came was that you didn't really *like* the labor in the first place.

Why not stay home until you feel the pressure of the baby's head on your rectum? Why rush to spend so much time in a lumpy bed with bunched-up sheets, where blue waterproof pads (chux) stick to your butt and give you "chux-marks"? Where the evening meal resembles Alpo?

Not that we feed you, of course. Once you are admitted to L&D, the standard is "NPO" (Nothing by mouth, or *nulli per os* in Latin).

Let's review:

Labor at term is an essentially normal event— something you've been expecting—hoping for, in truth—and something you knew all along was going to happen. Women do not die in labor, as a rule.

When it starts to happen to you, you immediately forget all of the above, and rush into the hospital so that you can:

1) starve;
2) lie flat on your back on polyester sheets in a lumpy twin bed with chux sticking to your ass;
3) pee into a bedpan;
4) get an IV and pain medication to stop your contractions;
5) get Pitocin to re-start your contractions.

Sometimes the beeper goes off at 11 p.m. as I am preparing to go to bed. Instantaneous nausea. What can it be? Will I be up all night? Who is it?

> *Pls call Maria Y re: just gave birth*
> *and she very constipated 718-555-8429*

What a relief! A *postpartum* patient! No chance of having to go into the hospital for that one!

Sometimes the beeper goes off at 10 p.m. on Friday night of a holiday weekend:

> *Pls call Kathy Z. re she think*
> *she have urine track infection*
> *718-555-9820*

Kathy Z. is a Gyn patient, 32 years old.
"How long have you had these symptoms?"
"Since yesterday morning."

224

"Okay. Now it's 10 p.m. on a Friday of a holiday weekend…"

"I guess I just didn't think it was that bad."

"Do you know the number of an all-night pharmacy in your neighborhood?"

Sometimes I get paged in the middle of a movie, or while I'm at the gym. The "vibrate" mode is intense when you're not expecting it. Once I actually screamed out loud.

> *Esther Shulman pregnant*
> *on way to hosp.*

There I was, in the middle of an action-adventure flick spanning three continents, on the Upper West Side on a Sunday afternoon, and Esther, pregnant with her seventh baby, was leaving Williamsburg for the hospital in downtown Brooklyn. Whatever happened to a little warning? A little lead-time? Do patients actually believe that we *live* in the hospital, camping on the floor of the office in our nightgowns, with little telephone headsets on, 24 hours a day, seven days a week?

Once at 3:45 a.m. I got a page from a patient with "a question about labor."

"Sharon? It's Sarah. What can I do for you?"

(*This better be good.*)

"Oh, hi Sarah! How are you? Is it busy there?"

"Is it busy *here*? In my *apartment*? In my *bedroom*? In the *dark*? Well, the cats are sleeping, I was sleeping…"

"Oh, I'm so sorry. I thought you'd be in the hospital."

"Sharon. Think for a minute. There are three midwives in the practice. We see patients in the office three days a week, we work in Labor & Delivery five days a week, and we sleep from time to time. When we're on call at night, we're generally at home, sleeping or having a life, unless someone's in labor. *We don't live in the hospital.* Are you in labor? "

"Oh, God, no. I'm so sorry. I just had a question. It can wait."

What the hell was she doing up at 3:45 a.m. anyway?

Sometimes when I am on call, the beeper doesn't go off at all. Not once, the entire night.

I wake up the next day feeling like I robbed a bank.

I was on call *and I got away with it!*

That means I've been given a whole extra day— the day after being on call—when I don't have to sleep, but can go to the gym, or see two movies in a row, or do anything I feel like. A whole extra day has been given to me.

Julianne is pacing the hallway outside of Triage when I arrive. It is a little after 4. I shake Seth's hand, give Julianne a hug. She appears calm, but cannot seem to relax her shoulders.

"What happened to your neck?" I joke, rubbing her shoulders.

Julianne is six centimeters dilated.

Amazing.

The ability to accurately self-diagnose active labor is not something American women are known for. Ireland, in fact, boasts the highest per capita rate of correct self-diagnosis of true labor— probably because Irish women don't make a big deal of it and therefore don't need to call it what it isn't—active labor—until it is.

We Americans, on the other hand, make such a huge drama of it, admonishing the labor partner to *time the contractions!* from the moment they begin, and describing in breathtaking detail the characteristics of contractions in childbirth classes. Whole hours are devoted to teaching pregnant women how to *breathe* once they are in labor. No wonder, then, that some of my patients' partners come in as exhausted and tense as their laboring spouses, brandishing raggedy scrolls of paper upon which is written nothing more than:

> 1:34
> 2:11
> 2:17
> 2:44
> 2:59
> 3:13 …

… and so on, representing hours and hours of fastidious notation. This scroll is offered to the midwife as evidence of labor.

It's not at all mysterious why American women typically present themselves to Labor & Delivery hours too early. The simple act of timing the contractions, with its intense focus on *every single contraction*, lengthens the hours of early labor into a sort of lifetime.

I advise my patients not to time the contractions under any circumstances when they are in labor, but to call the midwife when they can no longer hold a conversation.

By 6:30, Julianne is almost fully dilated. She has spent the entire time on all fours on the bed, rhythmically arching and curling her lower back—the yoga exercise known as "Cat/Cow." She makes no sound. Seth sits in a lounge chair by the bed, rubbing her feet and ankles.

Sometimes the midwife is completely superfluous. Julianne, for example, could do this almost entirely on her own, I am certain. All she would need was someone—anyone—to lift the baby out.

Other patients needed the comfort of the midwife's presence: a calm, authoritative voice, an experienced observer able to reassure and make suggestions. Still others wanted the midwife to run the show entirely. They put themselves passively in our hands; indeed, they expected us to do all the work.

Alone among primates, human beings require assistance with the delivery of their offspring. Whereas lower primates have a pelvic shape that favors the baby delivering in a face-up position, the human pelvis tends to promote the face-down position of the fetus for delivery. A face-up delivery can, in theory, be accomplished by the mother herself. She simply bends forward and pulls the infant onto her belly.

But a baby facing down must first bend in a downward direction to escape the bony cage of the mother's pelvis. Thus an assistant must be present, theoretically, to help the human baby into the world—or at least, to keep it from falling on the floor.

I saw once, on a nature program on television, a captive mountain gorilla giving birth. She lay on her back on the floor of her cage, writhing silently. As the baby's little head delivered, face up, its eyes locked onto its mother's face. She reached down and expertly pulled him onto her chest. Then, holding him in her arms, she rolled around on the floor in ecstasy.

When Julianne opted to stay on all fours for the delivery of her baby, I simply pushed the baby, cord and all, through her legs after I suctioned him and wiped the mucus from his face. Julianne took him, confidently, and turned onto her side.

Inmate

The Heights Medical Center is conveniently located in downtown Brooklyn, close to shopping, transportation, and Central Booking.

When a woman prisoner with a pregnant belly is taken to Central Booking for arraignment, if she has half a brain, chances are she will engage in "incarceration avoidance behavior." This entails holding one's lower abdomen, feigning great pain, and demanding to be brought to the nearest hospital.

The police of New York City had a terrible reputation during the mid- to late 1990s. An unarmed Guyanese man had been shot to death in a parking lot for "suspicious behavior," and another had been beaten so severely by the police during a peaceful protest march that he had required temporary kidney dialysis.

I was as dismayed as anyone when the New York cops began to be tarnished by these terrible scandals. My friend Rose, a prosecutor in the Bronx and a liberal like me, swore that it was a matter of a few bad apples spoiling the whole bushel.

"Your average cop," Rose said, "he's honest, hardworking, brave, and would never take a bribe."

I had my doubts. The man who was shot in the parking lot was a father of five, a quiet man with a green card who worked double shifts in a box factory so he could send money back to his family. He had a right to be in the parking lot. The police stopped him because he "resembled someone implicated in a robbery."

Leticia Adams was twenty weeks pregnant with her third child when she was arrested in a Rite Aid drugstore in downtown Brooklyn for shoplifting a bag of Cheetos, a Mistic mint tea, a can of Planter's Cocktail Peanuts and a Revlon lip gloss. Normally this would not entail a criminal arraignment, but Leticia already had a criminal record consisting of soliciting (twice) and drug possession (marijuana, less than two ounces).

Some time before arraignment, Leticia began complaining of "stomach pain and pressure," requiring the arresting officers to bring her to the Heights.

She was a sad-looking black woman, her hands cuffed behind her back, her hair matted down on one side, her clothes dirty, smelling of stale cigarette smoke and sweaty feet.

The nurses resented taking care of prisoners because 99.9 percent of the time it was completely bogus, a waste of time and an "abuse of the system."

Leticia had tear- and snot-trails down her face, and she refused to look at me. The arresting officer stood next to the exam table while the nurse put her on it. He undid the cuffs to help her onto the stretcher, then he cuffed her right hand to the railing.

I asked to speak with him outside the room.

"What's she done, Officer?"

P.O. Layden shrugged sheepishly.

"She was caught shoplifting at Rite Aid."

"For this we are cuffing her to the stretcher? Come on, Officer, have a heart, she's pregnant!"

"She has a criminal record, Miss," he said nervously.

"Ms. Adams, my name is Sarah Porter. I am a midwife. I need to ask you some questions. How old are you?"

Leticia refused to answer, or to look at me.

"Ms. Adams, I want to help you, but I can't if you don't tell me what the problem is."

No response.

"Ms. Adams, please tell me what's bothering you so I can try to help you."

Pause, then:

"I got stomach pains!"

"Show me where?"

Leticia motioned to her lower abdomen.

"When did you eat last?"

It seemed that Leticia had not eaten for several days. She had left her two-year-old daughter (her other kid was in foster care) with a neighbor to come to a food bank in Chelsea. There a social worker had told her about a job opening at a Wendy's at the Fulton Mall in downtown Brooklyn.

After taking the train to Brooklyn Heights and walking several blocks to the Fulton Mall, Leticia told me, she stood in the line at Wendy's among forty or fifty people waiting to be interviewed. The food she had gotten at the food bank was in two large paper shopping bags, one of which was already tearing.

After two and a half hours of waiting, the people still in line were told that the job had been filled. Leticia was so disgusted that she forgot her shopping bags, leaving them by the wall leading to the manager's office. She didn't realize this until she was several blocks away, by the Rite Aid.

Leticia told me all of this as I did her physical exam and started an IV. Sitting upright on the narrow stretcher, her hand cuffed to the railing, she broke into sobs from time to time as she told her story.

"You don't know what it's like, Miss," she said, newly aggrieved as she recounted her terrible day to me. "Waiting on line just to get some little peanut butter sandwiches wrapped in wax paper. Powdered milk my daughter won't even drink. Canned beans. Some dry-ass old cereal you wouldn't even recognize."

She stopped, leaning forward on the stretcher, and wiped her eyes with the bottom of her gown.

"I coulda had that job. I ain't had a job for two years, Miss. If only I woulda heard about it sooner..."

I palpated Leticia's belly. It was *soft and non-tender*; a little small for the due date she had given. I did a vaginal exam—her cervix was long and closed (not effaced and not dilated). Her stomach pains were clearly from hunger and misery only, not preterm labor.

I ordered her an early dinner tray and let her IV run wide open. She was so dehydrated her urine was the color of iced tea.

In the hallway, P.O. Layden sat patiently in a chair. He had been there for two hours already.

"Please uncuff her so she can eat," I insisted.

Reluctantly, P.O. Layden did so.

"What's going to happen to her, Officer?" I asked.

He sighed deeply. "If she's released by the hospital, she'll go back to Night Court to be arraigned. Once she's arraigned, unless she makes bail, she'll spend the night in the Brooklyn Detention Center, or Rikers, or another holding facility to await a Grand Jury hearing."

"All of this for some Mistic Mint and Cheetos?"

P.O. Layden shrugged and gave me a sad smile. "She has priors, Miss."

Leticia tore into the hospital dinner tray as though it was the *plat du jour* at Lutèce. Hunching over eagerly in her faded blue hospital gown, she attacked the food, making inadvertent low grunting sounds. This was the same food that patients routinely returned uneaten, the food whose foul aromas bothered the sensitive pregnant women who had to endure them.

What would have to happen to alleviate Leticia's burdens? What *deus ex machina* would descend from the catwalks to make her life livable?

I released her to police custody.

"Leticia, I'm going to let you go now," I said. "The baby seems fine. I think you were just terribly dehydrated and hungry." I pulled the IV catheter out of her arm as I addressed her.

P.O. Layden knocked politely on the door as Leticia was pulling on her clothes.

"Ready, Miss Adams?"

She gave a reluctant nod.

"Will I be able to call my neighbor when we get back? I don't know who's going to take care of my daughter."

"Call now if you want," P.O. Layden said, gesturing to the phone.

"Thank you, Miss," Leticia said to me as she joined the police officers in the hall. She had worked out that her neighbor would watch over her daughter for the night, and her boyfriend would pick the kid up in the morning.

P.O. Layden turned to his partner.

"Gimme your cuffs."

He linked the two pairs of handcuffs together.

"I'm doubling the cuffs so you won't have to put your arms so far back," he explained to Leticia. Gently he drew her arm behind her back and placed the first handcuff on her right wrist.

"Turn your hand," he said. "I don't want to pinch your skin."

In this manner they left.

Basketball Jones

"To think that when children do this, it's cute," Moe remarked.

We stood aghast at the sidelines of the court, watching our teammates running up and down, up and down, leaping in the air like cartoon hippopotamuses and giraffes, swatting at each other's faces and elbowing each other.

Thank God, at least I have small breasts, I thought.

Rose, who was a year-round athlete, had persuaded Moe and me to take a beginning adult basketball clinic. Rose had played Division III ball in college as a walk-on, and Moe had played high school basketball. It was I who was the anti-athlete.

The last time I had played basketball was in junior high. Even then, I had shown no talent for it. I remembered jamming my pinky and the gym teacher refusing to let me sit out the game. The next day when I showed up with a cast on my finger, she turned pale and broke into a sweat.

All my memories of adolescent sports, in fact, were wrapped around evil gym teachers screaming at me, or always being picked last for the softball team, or feeling sick to my stomach when ordered to sub in. Playing sports seemed to come easily to everyone but me and the other members of my family.

"It'll be fun," Rose had pleaded.

"Are you out of your mind? Think of ankle sprains, back injuries, facial lacerations…"

"It's really fun," Moe insisted. "We'll meet men there. Plus, we're getting all out of shape from working so much and eating at Taco Bell all the time."

She was right. I had never been this fat before. The hospital had a Taco Bell in its lobby, and that was where we ended up eating almost every day.

The basketball clinic was run by a short, wiry, demonically energetic man named Jacques, whose credentials included having been an assistant coach on the Princeton men's basketball team of 1983, the year the Tigers made it to the second round of the NCAA tournament. The clinic was held on Monday nights at a high-school gym on the Lower East Side.

Jacques stood at the sidelines, whistle perpetually in mouth, and screamed orders at us.

"High post—screen away!"

"Three-man weave, full court—*three passes only*! Go *behind* the passer! *Is* anybody *listening to me?*"

I felt like a complete ass most of the time, but it was fun, there were men there and to my amazement, I did not get winded easily. Sometimes I was the first one to get back on defense. *Me!*

I had already signed up to take the intermediate clinic after this one finished. I was hooked. I was reading the pro basketball coverage in the Daily News and watching Knicks games on television. I had a framed poster of Charles Oakley on my bedroom wall.

Then Jacques decided to get personal.

"Sarah!" You're playing out of position!" The players froze as Jacques' whistle sounded.

It was the fourth week of the clinic. Already I had spent several hundred dollars on shoes, long shorts and sleeveless jerseys. I was starting to lift weights—I wanted to have cut arms like the pro players I watched. I had bought a leather indoor-outdoor regulation Spalding, and I was starting to research gyms that had full courts.

I wish he'd swallow that thing.

"Sarah! That's not how you set a pick! Don't stick your butt out like that!"

"Sarah! You have your back to the basket! You're not even looking for the ball!"

"Now, that's how *not* to play defense, Sarah. People! You play defense with your feet, not your hands!"

How convenient for Jacques, I thought, running back upcourt, my face beet-red, *to have someone like me to demonstrate all the things you're* not *supposed to do.*

I mean, really! Was there no one else in the clinic who ever did anything wrong? It was beginning basketball, for God's sake!

Finally, six weeks into it, when I the nausea I had begun to feel Monday nights on the way to the gym was becoming all too familiar, I confronted Jacques during a timeout.

"Hey, guess what, Jacques? I'm paying you two hundred dollars to learn to play basketball and have *fun*," I said. I was panting hoarsely, and my eyes were watering. *Oh, great. Just what he needs to see. Sarah can't hack it. She's a crybaby.*

"Yes, and…?"

"I'm not being paid to play. I'm not on an athletic scholarship!" My voice was taking on an hysterical edge. Some of the other players were looking over. Moe eyed me anxiously and whispered something to Rose. Rose looked embarrassed.

"Thank God for that," Jacques said.

"That's what I'm talking about!" I could feel tears stinging my eyes. It was just like fifth grade again, when everyone avoided looking at me while choosing up sides for kickball.

"What's your problem, Sarah?"

"My problem is, I can't take you yelling at me all the time! Find another scapegoat! I don't respond to this tough-love shit! I'm an adult! This is supposed to be fun, not painful! If I wanted to be criticized, I 'd call my mother or something!" I dabbed at my eyes with the bottom of my sweaty t-shirt.

The force of my rage hit Jacques like a tidal wave. He recoiled. Then he seemed to reconsider. His face softened. He actually looked affectionate for a minute.

"Maybe you're right, Sarah. I was just trying to coach you my way, but maybe my way is not the best way everyone for this group. Believe me, if I didn't think you had potential, I wouldn't single you out all the time."

"Can't you ever say anything positive to me? The way you do about Moe and Rose and the others? I mean, only if I deserve it."

"Sure I can. Don't worry about it. Just get back in the game, Sarah."

Okay, I sucked at offense, but I played ferocious defense, which Jacques took great pains to point out to everyone. I was developing a sweet little 10-foot set shot. I joined a gym in my neighborhood with a full court, and I begged the men to let me join them in their play-to-fifteen/win-by-two scrimmages when they needed a player to make ten. Then my defender would guard me so gingerly I would be forced to taunt him:

Is that *how you play defense?*

Or,

Oh, I'm sorry. Were you guarding me?

Or:

Afraid I'll hurt you?

This would irritate the guy, get into his head, and make him guard me like anybody else. This forced me to play tougher, basically to avoid being killed or maimed.

I was desperate to improve my skills before I got too old to play. Why had I only discovered basketball so late in life? Why had I formerly shunned jocks, assuming they were limited or dumb? The jocks I was meeting now were way more interesting —and better-looking—than many of the so-called intellectuals I had known in college, for example.

For the first time in my life, I was doing something—well, *sporty*—and I liked it! This was a revelation on a par with my decision long ago to leave journalism because something was missing in my life. Walking onto the court with my teammates after a time out, taping my ankles in the locker room before a game, talking trash—it made me feel powerful and alive.

I signed up with a trainer at my gym for basketball coaching sessions at $40 an hour. Over time, my shooting percentage improved. On my days off I would go to the gym in my sagging, shiny shorts and $140 Grant Hill shoes to systematically shoot 100 layups, left, right, left, right, then 200 free throws, then a game of Around the World, shooting from all the spots, kicking myself back to the beginning if I missed a shot.

It was my new obsession.

"Sarah, looking good!" Frantz said.

Frantz, my coach, was six foot two, Haitian-American, thin and muscular, with a deep, hoarse voice. His hair was done in little twists. I was crazy about him.

Frantz didn't seem to mind me either. Sometimes when I "posted him up," backing into him near the basket to set up for a drop-step-la-yup move, I would feel his partial tumescence blossoming against my lower back. This made for some interesting one-on-one games.

("We should definitely incorporate this into our strategy when we play with men," Moe said.)

Eventually, Frantz and I made out—first standing against the wall of the supply closet at the gym, which smelled of mildew, old socks and perspiration, and later, lying on my sofa, which smelled slightly of cat puke.

Frantz murmured in Creole as he stroked me.

"I don't get it. Weren't you born here?" I asked. "How is it you know Creole?"

"All Haitian-American children learn Creole at the dinner table," Frantz muttered in my ear as he unbuttoned my blouse.

"Where can I learn Creole?"

"Why do you want to learn Creole?"

"Because a bunch of my patients speak it, and it would really help if I could communicate in their language. Plus, I was thinking of going to Haiti as a volunteer health-care worker."

"I know someone who can teach you Creole," Frantz said, his voice raspy with lust. "How about I tell you later?"

Creole Lesson

Deye mon, gen mon. (Behind the mountain, there is another mountain.)

Li pa gen djòb. (He doesn't have a job.)

Timoun yo grangou anpil. (The children are very hungry.)

Madanm nan gen tifoid, epi li pa kapab pale anglé. (The lady has typhoid, and she can't speak English.)

Li gen diaré, docté. (She has diarrhea, Doctor.)

Map boulé. (I'm burning.)

Map luté. (I'm struggling.)

Map dégaje'm. (I'm doing the best I can.)

Nou bezwen mangé. (We need food.)

Bourik la tonbe, paske le gen lafièv. (The donkey falls, because he has fever.)

"Pasté Louis, pou ki sa tout frasé yo tris?" I asked falteringly. (Pastor Louis, why are all these phrases sad?)

Good to his word, Frantz had sent me to Pasté Louis to learn Creole. Weekly I took the train to Flatbush, Brooklyn, where Pasté Louis shared an apartment with another Haitian family. Pasté Louis's wife and daughters still lived in Haiti, but they were applying for visas. Pasté Louis was the minister of a small evangelical church in the neighborhood. He had written a "Learn Creole" textbook on a manual typewriter. I paid him $30 an hour for lessons. My Haitian patients in the Ob/Gyn clinic were excited that I was learning Creole and going to Haiti, and any halting attempt on my part to speak Creole with them was met by enthusiastic, rapid-fire replies that I could not understand.

Pasté Louis had worked as a translator at a large hospital in the Haitian countryside. He was helping me apply to go there as a volunteer. I had saved all my vacation and sick time so that I could take a month off, and Susan was giving me an additional two weeks' unpaid leave.

I wasn't sure what I wanted from this experience. I only knew I wasn't satisfied with my life the way it was. Being a midwife—playing catch, as Steven had dubbed it long ago—was good, but it didn't make me feel the way I thought it should. I wanted an epiphany, a conversion experience. I wanted to do something so important that my life would change inexorably. I wanted to stop thinking about me all the time.

Pasté Louis smiled at me. *"Ou panse ke frasé yo tris?"* (Do you think these phrases are sad?)

"Wi. Pou ki sa?" (Yes. Why?)

He sighed. *"Lavi Ayisien é du anpil."* (Life in Haiti is very hard.)

He continued in English:

"Life in Haiti is hard, but the Haitians are a beautiful, hard-working, loving people. When you go to the hospital, you will be surrounded by Americans and Europeans and Canadians. The volunteers are almost all *blans* [foreigners] and so are most of the permanent staff. It will be very tempting for you to spend all your free time with people like yourself. But I hope you will make friends with real Haitians, and get to know their way of life. Your experience will be much richer for it."

Lesson Five:

<u>Translate this Haitian folk song into English:</u>

Fèy, o. sove lavi mwen. Nan mizè mwen ye o…
Pitit mwen malad; mwen kouri kay gangan –
Si li bon gangan…
Li sove lavi mwen. Nan mizè mwen ye…

(Leaf, oh, save my life. I am in such misery!

My child is sick. I run to the house of the voodoo priest…

If he is a good priest, he will save my life. I am in such misery!)

246

Ayiti Cheri

Ayiti Cheri,
Pi bon peyi pase ou lanpwen.
Fòk mwen te kite ou pou mwen te kap konprann valè ou;
Fòk mwen te manke ou pou'm te kap apresye ou
Pou'm santi vreman tout sa ou te ye pou mwen

Gen bon soley, bon rivye e bon brevaj
Anba pie boua ou toujou jwenn bol lonbraj
Gen bon ti van ki bannou bon ti frechè
Ayiti cheri, se yon peyi ki me cher.

Beloved Haiti,
A better country than you there is not;
I had to leave you to understand your value.
I had to miss you to be able to appreciate you,
To really feel all you are to me.

There is good sunshine, good riv-
ers and fine nectars,
Underneath a tree, you always find good shade.

There is a good little breeze to
give you sweet fresh air.
Beloved Haiti is a very dear country to me.

February 10, 1997, St. George, Haiti

Dear Moe:

Do you have any t-shirts with slogans or symbols on them that you don't want? Can you ship them to me here ASAP? I need them for going-away presents when I leave.

Haitians <u>love</u> American t-shirts. It's not clear to me where the t-shirts come from, except that they definitely come from America. It is doubtful that the t-shirts I've seen here come from Christian charity groups, since most say things like:

"Screw Housework, Let's Go Bingo"

"I'm Going Nucking Futs"

"Kill 'Em All ... Let God Sort 'Em Out"

"I Don't Have a Drinking Problem. I Drink, I Fall Down. No   Problem."

My favorites include:

"It's Just Your Attitude"

"When Smith & Wesson Talk ... People Listen"

"I'm a Party Waiting to Happen"

"You May Say I'm a Dreamer, But I'm Not the Only One"

"For Pete's Sake, Give Blood"

... and the ever-enigmatic "Jim Loves Sue"

Today in the Adult Medicine clinic an old man came in for his insulin injection wearing a brown polyester baseball cap with "Shithead" emblazoned across the front. Of course, he had no idea what his cap said. I couldn't look at him while I was giving him his shot. I was afraid I would start laughing uncontrollably.

Hats are *de rigueur* here. The sun is constant and punishing. The other day I saw two middle-aged men strolling down the main street here, hand in hand, both wearing stunning polyester "straw" hats with sequins and black veils. Here where it's hot, a hat is a hat, and that's that. Even I, who look like a giant insect in hats, am forced to wear one – a to'-up old straw thing with a big floppy brim that Lydia gave me just before I left New York.

It's "dry season" now, meaning that the brief rainy season has just ended., It means the Pediatrics ward won't be seeing too much kwashiorkor for another couple of months, until the agricultural effects of the dry season start to show up. Because the rainy season has just finished, crops are relatively plentiful, and gardens are still producing. (By "relatively plentiful," I mean that a family of six can possibly get two small meals a day from a garden.)

Do you remember kwashiorkor from nursing school? Or can you recall those photo spreads in Time magazine or National Geographic years ago, from countries like Biafra and Bangladesh? Those little, red-skinned, red-haired, skeletal, pot-bellied children staring unflinchingly at the camera? Here it's commonplace among young children after they are weaned, because they can't get any protein in their diets. In another two to three months, the Peds ward will be packed with kwash babies; for now, AIDS, malaria, sepsis, bacterial meningitis and chronic diarrhea are the diagnoses *du jour* in Peds.

It is so dry and so hot that during the course of a typical workday, the dust collects on your face, mixes with your sweat and forms a sort of cake mix, which you discover at the end of the day when you attempt to wash said face. When the trucks go by in the road, the dust they leave in their wake is so thick you can't see in front of you for minutes.

It rained the other evening, miraculously, for about half an hour, while I was assisting one of the pediatricians with a spinal tap on a two-year-old with suspected meningitis. The people at the hospital—staff, patients, visitors, everyone—were so surprised that those who could walk shuffled outside to the courtyard and stood, mouths agape, staring up at the sky.

The pediatrician and I had moved the procedure table out into the courtyard to get some air, and when the rain began to fall we were so stunned we just stood there, him poking at the by-now-silent little boy, me holding the kid's shoulders and little skinny bottom in a C-curve while the French pediatrician poked and poked and poked away at him and the rain fell down like a blessing.

It's nine o'clock and I'm going to try to go to bed now—work starts at 7 a.m. and I don't sleep too well here.

I love you, I miss you. Please write soon.

Shopping list, 2/14/97:

        4 Coca-cola (6 gdes each) – 24 gdes*
        6 Prestige (12 gdes each) - 72 gdes
        saltines 1 box   - 25 gdes
plantain 1 bunch   - 10 gdes
        matches   ?
        writing paper ?
        flashlight batteries ?
        lèt – 1 box   ?   [there is no such thing as fresh milk in St. George, only powdered]
        cooking oil
        snacks ???

Diary excerpt, 2/15/97:

I am so hungry every day—I, the rich fat *blan* [foreigner] who gets three meals a day, guaranteed, cooked by the lovely Mireille—that I dream of food every night. I cannot possibly imagine what it must be like to be Haitian, with no guaranteed meals at all.

I weigh myself weekly in the Peds ward. My last weight was 55 kgs, down from 59 when I arrived. That's 121 lbs.—I haven't weighed that little since high school.

* a gourde, abbreviated gde., is the main currency of Haiti. Five gourdes equal one "Haitian dollar," which is worth very little.

The little commissary on the grounds of the hospital occasionally sells American-type snacks, such as Goldfish and Ritz bits. I buy and hoard these things like mad when I can. There just isn't that much to eat, period, and what there is comes in very small quantities. However, although I may be really skinny and fantasizing constantly about giant plates of pasta, I am aware that I am fortunate to be able to rely on eating as often as I do.

2/25/97:

I live in *Lakay Vèt* [the Green House], the hospital's short-stay volunteer residence. It is a large, single-story low-ceilinged four-bedroom house made of bright green painted stucco, with metal bars on the windows and a small concrete slab for a porch. Goats graze in the yard, and sometimes wander onto the porch by accident and knock into the door by mistake. Lakay Vèt sits just behind a stand of trees that separates the hospital grounds from the *ti maché* [the little market. The "big market," or *gwo mache,* is several towns away.].

The *ti mache* is open Mondays from 5 a.m. till 3 p.m., and Friday afternoons from noon until about 6, although there is nothing in the ti maché that you'd want to buy. Every morning except Sundays, at 5:30 a.m. on the grounds of the market, a single pig is slaughtered, very slowly.

These poor creatures' sufferings are my alarm clock. It is both fitting and horrific to wake up every day in this country that has been all but destroyed by cruelty, where cruelty is a way of life, to hear a poor mammal screaming its last for 45 minutes or more. Apparently the ritual way of slaughtering animals here involves doing it very, very slowly. Sometimes long after I am certain the pig has shuffled off this mortal coil, it will let out one last scream.

It's really almost unbearable to wake up to this every day. One of the guest surgeons who stayed across the hall from me for a week bitched like mad about it. She got the hospital director involved and everything. As if you could ask these poor people to change their ways to make *us* more comfortable:

Mesié, si vous plais. Nou pap mange kochon, epi nou rinmin tout bèt. Eske ou kapab pa touye kochon yo?

Sir, if you please. We do not eat pork, and we revere all animals. Can you please stop slaughtering these pigs?

2/28/97:

I was invited this afternoon to go with Jenny and Felix to the nearby town of Boulé to play pickup basketball after work. Jenny is the Haitian-American woman who works in the Community Affairs department of the hospital, organizing the agribusiness programs, and Felix is her Haitian husband. They have two girls, Michèle, six, a Haitian orphan whom they adopted two years ago, and Marie, who is five.

The little girls and I rode in the back of Felix's pickup on the short ride to Boulé, with Bob Marley blasting from the cab:

> *Feel it in the one drop,*
> *And we'll still find time to rap,*
> *We're making the one stop*
> *The generation gap,*
> *So feel dis drum-beat*
> *As it beats within,*
> *Playing a riddum,*
> *Resistin' against the system*

Haiti is a country where physical discomfort is a constant fact of daily life. Although I am fortunate to escape many discomforts experienced by most Haitians every day—such as hunger—I get my share nonetheless.

There are a host of side effects to chloroquin phosphate, the anti-malarial I'm taking, including muscle stiffness, nausea, vomiting, diarrhea, abdominal pain, headache, itching, fatigue, weakness, tinnitus, hearing loss, sleep disturbances and "personality changes," and I've got nearly every one of them. I sleep with a large electric fan pointing at my face all night, which gives me a stiff neck and blows the loose hair around my face, creating the sensation of tiny insects crawling on me. Work entails sweating from sunup until sundown, accumulating layer upon layer of dirt and dust, rendering painful, torturous treatments to suffering children, and trying desperately to understand the deep, primitive, mumbly "mountain Creole" spoken by most of the patients here. Thanks to the quality of the roads, riding in vehicles is like being jounced inside a bag of stones.

On the road to Boulé, we bounced so high in the flatbed I was afraid for the girls' safety.

"Ba'm min ou!" I commanded them. (Give me your hands!)

To my great shock, they obeyed. As I clutched their sticky little hands, the realization washed over me like a tidal wave: Oh my God, *I'm speaking Creole and Haitian children understand me!*

3/1/97:

Susan wrote me today. She reminded me that last week she deposited the last of my vacation paychecks. The next three weeks, until I come home, are unpaid leave. She said the practice misses me, the patients miss me, and she misses me. Her husband, David, got pneumonia and was hospitalized for five days, and there's some new badness between the midwife practice and the administration, apparently having to do with a patient being allowed to push for 6 hours and 20 minutes. Although she delivered vaginally, her nurse felt compelled to write an "incident report." Always after the midwives! If a doctor had done the same thing, he'd be a hero now.

Here in St. George, I am so far removed from all that, I can scarcely imagine worrying about such things.

3/3/97:

The Bob Marley tune from the truck keeps playing in my head:

> *They made the world so hard*
> *Every day we got to keep on fighting*
> *They made the world so hard*
> *Every day the people are dying*

Today a little boy, Rubens, who had been in a coma for more than a week, woke up. Rubens had bacterial meningitis and his prognosis is very poor. By the time his parents carried him here from his village in the mountains, his temperature was 105.

"His bwain is fwied," the French pediatrician had said matter-of-factly as the nurses rolled Rubens onto a stretcher.

He's been receiving heavy-duty antibiotics and steroids since he got here, but the consensus has been that Rubens will not be himself again, if he lives at all.

But today Rubens woke up and murmured something in Creole to the nurse standing at his bedside. She was so startled she dropped the tray of meds she was holding.

On the floor next to Rubens' bed, his father, a lively, smiling man in a white straw hat, plaid shirt and black wool pants, sat and read aloud to the children of the Peds ward from a tattered Creole Bible. His voice rose with each exciting passage, falling to a whisper to indicate his reverence for the miracles of which he spoke. I could occasionally catch remnants of the text—he chose mostly miracle stories: Daniel in the lion's den; the feeding of the five thousand, the wedding at Cana. He calls me *sage femme* (literally, "wise woman", the French term for midwife).

3/4/97:

The first thing I noticed about the baby was its eyelashes. It had impossibly long eyelashes, so that the upper ones, still slick with amniotic fluid and that cheesy white stuff, *vernix caseosa*, that coats the skins of babies in utero, tangled in the lower ones.

It was trying to open its eyes, but the sticky goo held its lids shut. It was squirming and making weak mewling sounds, like a newborn kitten. It had shot out of its mother a few moments before without warning.

The nurse went off to get a delivery set. The baby kept mewing. I saw that it was a girl. She struggled mightily—she was about the size of a Pepperidge Farm Cocktail Loaf—and then her eyes opened.

She was a beautiful baby, and she kept on breathing despite the grim plans we had made for her that morning. Without gloves, I was reluctant to touch her, but I lifted her onto the mother's abdomen for warmth. The mother was also making sounds, but nothing I could understand. Flies swarmed around her, occasionally landing on her head. Her face was so swollen she couldn't open her eyes.

The baby's mother had been admitted to the hospital 24 hours earlier. Information was sketchy, but she had apparently suffered two seizures at home—the seizures of *eclampsia* [usually preventable in the States but commonplace here in the Third World]. Her family brought her from her home in the mountains miles away, propped up on the back of a tiny horse. Her husband was now nowhere to be found. He had gone back to return the little horse to the neighbor, who needed it for plowing, and was presumably making his way back to the hospital on foot. Her sister-in-law, who remained with her, knew almost nothing about the woman and spoke the deep, primitive Creole that all the locals spoke—words all run together in an unintelligible blah-blah-blah. The patient was obviously pregnant, but from the size of her belly it was clear the fetus was not viable.

"There's no way this baby is full-term," I told John, the visiting Ob/Gyn from Seattle, that morning. "This baby cannot possibly live, and we need to deliver this woman or she'll die."

"I agree absolutely," John said. "Let's Pit her out."

So the plan was to induce labor with Pitocin, to assume the baby was not viable, and to expedite the delivery. We agreed not to bother listening to the baby's heartbeat during the induction, because we weren't going to act on that information anyway. Even if the induced labor caused distress in the fetus, we weren't going to perform a cesarean to save the baby when the baby couldn't possibly be saved. In the States, a severely premature baby has a reasonable chance of surviving with brain function and organs intact, but here the life of a premature baby is of no consequence. You act to save the mother only. We couldn't really share this information with the mother, because she was so obtunded from the seizures that she was barely conscious.

In the past two days, three premature babies have died here. I watched one lying in the little warmer he shared with another preemie, struggling for air, his tiny chest heaving, during the hours before he died.

Yet here was this miniature baby, not premature but *growth-restricted*, looking pink and vigorous.

John came strolling up the hall. He saw me and stopped for a moment, his expression quizzical.

"She delivered?"

"Take a look."

We stood and beheld the baby on the mother's belly.

"Looks pretty good," John said. "What's your plan?"

I sighed. "I'm waiting for the nurse to bring a delivery set so I can cut the cord and take her to Peds. They're going to kill me. Another preemie for them to deal with."

"Maybe not. She looks pretty good. Maybe she's just growth restricted."

3/5/97:

Manithé asked me today how to say in English *"fe bagay-a"* ["do the thing"]. She was swirling around the Pediatric nurses' station. It was four o'clock and her shift was ending.

"I don't know. *Fuck*?"

"Okay, Say-rah. I go 'ome to *make fuck* weeth my 'usband."

This is our running joke. When I leave each day, at the end of the shift, I say, in English, "I'm going home to..." and fill in the blank with some outrageous activity not possible here in St. George, such as "watch television," or "eat a huge steak," or "kill the *tontons macoutes* [the former Haitian secret police, responsible for the deaths of thousands of civilians from the late '50s until recently]."

Rubens is coming along. He walks now, with help, but he cannot speak clearly.

"Li fache anpil jodi-a," his father informed me solemnly, as I stood at his bedside (He is very angry today).

I think he meant that Rubens was frustrated because of all the things he wanted to do and say that the remnants of his disease would not permit. The fever seemed to have permanently damaged the speaking part of his cerebral cortex, while the moving-around part was coming back slowly.

Manithé calls Rubens "*ti diab*" (little devil) and tickles him to try to get him to speak, but everything comes out garbled.

Manithé, Laurie and Judith are the nurses I work with most of the time on Pediatrics and Medicine. They all attended the same nursing school in Port-au-Prince. They are wicked smart. They are also nice, cute, fun-loving young girls who want to learn English and who don't resent me for being a rich *blan*. Some of the other people here blatantly resent me.

I figured it out a few nights ago when I was a little drunk on "Prestige," the local beer. Although I have taken great pains to tell everyone at the hospital that I am a volunteer, that I am not getting paid, that I am *not taking a job from a Haitian*, they still seem to resent me. But, of course, anyone who could afford to volunteer for six weeks without pay must be *riche anpil*! Duh! So I am the rich *blan* who came from New York to boss the nurses around. Or so they think. Except Manithé, Laurie and Judith.

3/12/97:

The growth-restricted baby, Angeline, thrived. Her mother, who suffered temporary blindness, regained her sight and did well. They left the hospital yesterday, on horseback.

Today Rubens, who is discharged to home, came up to me in the hall. He hugged me around the waist and tried to kiss me and pulled me by the hand. Mumbling something unintelligible, he pulled and pulled and pulled me towards the door.

"*Li rinmin ou anpil anpil*," his father said jovially. (He likes you a lot.)

I think Rubens was trying to take me home with him!

Laurie and Judith came over to Lakay Vèt tonight for their English lesson. They are applying for a grant to study pediatric nursing in Miami, but their English needs work. Since I arrived, they are making lightning-fast progress, they assure me. We are on "idioms and slang" now, and they are amazingly proficient.

"Laurie, let's go *grab a bite*," Judith said.

"Will you *foot the bill*?" Laurie came back snappily.

"No, I want to *go Dutch*!" Judith exclaimed triumphantly.

"Okay, *zanmi mwen* (my friends)," I said. "Here is a phrase I want you to memorize. When a man treats you badly, you are to cut your eyes at him and say, "*I am not accustomed to being treated in this fashion.*"

"I like that!" Laurie said. "Let me try it." She shook her head as if warding off evil thoughts, batted her eyelashes and said indignantly: "*I am not accustomed to being treated in this fascination!*"

3/10/97:

The lovely mail came! Frantz sent me a plastic basketball! After my shift, I went straight to the hospital garage to inflate it with the big electric air pump. The basketball court on the grounds of the hospital has one working hoop, but a person stands little chance of actually shooting around. If you have a ball, you must share it with the twenty or so kids who hang around the court all day long hoping someone with a ball will show up. Then when you want to leave the court, everyone asks you to give him the ball. I had to almost wrench the ball out of the hands of this one big kid who had been hogging it the whole time anyway. Nobody ever said being poor and hungry and bored makes you noble or selfless. I will give the basketball to Gerard when I leave, but it won't last long on that concrete.

3/11/97:

I will be back in New York in two and a half weeks.

After Grand Rounds today, I went to the Medicine Ward, where there was a pregnant patient that John, the visiting American Ob/Gyn, had admitted the day before for induction of labor.

The patient in question, a very sweet, nice, fat (by Haitian standards) lady of 32, was having her fifth baby and had mild preeclampsia [the pregnancy-induced disease of high blood pressure and nonspecific organ damage—the other lady, Angeline's mother, had a severe case of it, called *eclampsia*.].

She was already in active labor when I got there. They were giving her Pitocin to induce her labor, and I was determined to switch the Pitocin over to the new infusion pumps that were recently donated to the hospital, which nobody had tried to use yet. There are so many medications they give here in the main IV line that really should be given through a pump. It is a goal of mine to get the nurses using the pumps before I leave.

I tried to hear the baby's heartbeat with my wooden fetoscope, an old-fashioned, elegant instrument that I had used many times before, but I couldn't hear anything. It made me nervous, although Dr. Jean-Pierre swore he had heard the heartbeat yesterday afternoon. The patient admitted that the baby had moved last evening but not since.

As we were making "walking rounds" on her, it came to light that her last period was in late April, making her almost ten months pregnant! I told John I couldn't hear the fetus' heartbeat, and he admonished me: "We can't do a c-section just because we can't hear the fetal heart." Once again, the mother's safety is paramount, and the fetus' life is secondary. Bizarre, for a largely Catholic country. Poverty trumps religion.

We transferred the Pitocin from the mainline IV to the pump and the induction proceeded. Very soon she was fully dilated and pushing. Judith was off that day, and the two nurses I was working with, Suzie and Julienne, were nice enough, but fairly helpless.

Meanwhile, I had a bad feeling about the baby. As the head delivered, I knew it was going to be bad. I could already see that the baby's skin was peeling off—a very bad sign. So when the body delivered, I got what I expected—a huge, dead, full-term baby. Almost 10 pounds, I would guess.

All the Medicine docs—Jean-Pierre, Marcella and Vitti—had gathered around to watch and give advice.

I said, "This baby is dead." Vitti watched me for a minute, and then said, "You should take the baby to Pediatrics to resuscitate it," and I said firmly, "No. This baby is *dead*." Then I told the mother, who became hysterical, and the grandmother, likewise.

The grandmother was praying and murmuring, "*Jesu, Jesu*," and the mother was saying unintelligible things, and meanwhile it was completely obvious to me that the baby had not been dead for long. The skin was just starting to peel, the skull bones were firm as a rock and the whole picture was that of a baby that had been dead for no more than 12 hours. If we had had a working fetal monitor—if we had been monitoring the fetus throughout the labor—we would have undoubtedly seen signs of trouble yesterday and could have done a cesarean, and we might have had a live baby today.

I wiped the baby off and wrapped it and gave it to the mother for a minute. It was a boy, and he was beautiful to behold. His hands were draped over his chest in a pensive attitude, and he had long eyelashes that curled up to his eyebrows. I couldn't get over his hands, how big and perfect they were.

I kept asking the nurses what I should do with the baby, and they just shrugged. Finally the *Oxiliére*—the Haitian equivalent of a nurse's aide—showed up with a *cardboard box*—about a nine-inch cube—and said she would put the baby in the box and take him to the morgue. I said in loud English, because I could not find any Creole words anymore—"The baby will not fit in that box. I will carry him to the morgue."

With the grandmother following and murmuring to Jesu, the *Oxiliére* led us through the halls of the hospital to an outdoor room near the garage—a locked room—and yelled at someone to come and open it. A crowd of the curious followed us, including a teenage boy. I told them all to leave, but they ignored me. A man opened the room and ordered me in Creole to enter. It was a small, dank, filthy room with debris all over and an open incinerator filled with ashes and char and garbage. Everyone shouted at me to put the baby in the incinerator. I was shivering. I clutched the baby to my chest and said in English, over and over, *"You're joking. You don't mean this. I'm not going to do this,"* but they kept yelling at me, so finally I gave the baby one more look—God, he was beautiful—and laid him in the open incinerator. The Grandmother was chanting some sort of prayer, thanking Jesus, and she and I walked slowly back to the Medicine Ward with our arms around each other.

Later on, I asked Pasté Andre, the hospital chaplain, about the incinerator. I couldn't help thinking I had done a terrible thing. Pasté Andre explained that in Haitian culture, an infant is not considered to have lived until it has been alive for several days or weeks. Only then does it merit a burial.

"Burial is very expensive here," he pointed out. "A baby that dies in the womb is not considered to have a soul. So it is okay to put its body in an incinerator."

That evening, as I was leaving the hospital, I recognized the woman's family members coming into the lobby. They were chattering excitedly and carrying a blue plastic bin filled with freshly washed baby clothes.

The Labor Gods

"Hi, Sarah. Oh, God, I hope I'm dilated enough to go to the Birthing Center!"

A tall, heavyset woman wearing a shapeless skirt, flannel shirt and open-toed white sandals with bright-white tube socks stood behind Laura, rubbing her back. Jimmy, Laura's husband, hovered nearby, clutching several pillows and a huge duffel bag.

We were in the waiting area outside Triage. After lying fallow for six weeks while I was in Haiti, my beeper seemed to have sprung into overdrive. I had been called in for a delivery almost every night that I was on call since my return two weeks before.

Our hospital had recently built a "Birthing Center" down the hall from Labor & Delivery, featuring Jacuzzis, low lighting, soundproof tiles, queen-size beds and "a home-like atmosphere." That's what the brochures said, "a home-like atmosphere."

We midwives were happy to have an alternative for our patients who wanted to give birth in someone else's $700,000 "home" instead of Labor & Delivery, which more closely resembled Satan's home. The only trouble with the Birthing Center was that "Birthing Center candidates" assumed in advance that they'd have the kind of labor where no "interventions" would be required. This was often the case for second babies, but for first-time mothers, labor sometimes entailed days of irregular contractions at home—not enough to be called 'labor,' but enough to ensure no sleep—followed by hours of torturous labor in the hospital.

Sometimes we had no choice. A woman who had been contracting for three days without significant progress was a woman who would eventually need Pitocin and an epidural. Her uterus was exhausted and so was she. Without Pitocin to jump-start the uterus and an epidural to relax the mother, a cesarean was a definite possibility.

These women were often bitterly disappointed that they couldn't use the Birthing Center, where Pitocin and epidural were not an option. It was as though the very existence of the Birthing Center meant that all those women who signed up in their heads for a "home-like," low-lit, soundproof, Jacuzzi-type experience were *guaranteed* to have one.

Not so, said the Labor gods.

The Labor gods were ironic, mean-spirited guys. Yes, they were men. We Ob people feared and respected the Labor gods. It was a longstanding joke—just ask an Obstetrician or Labor & Delivery nurse. Any patient whose husband came to the hospital wearing a t-shirt that said "Coach," any patient carrying extra pillows, a hot-water bottle, snacks, a "birth plan" and/or a "Lamaze bag," was almost certain to wind up in the Operating Room for a cesarean delivery. The Labor gods didn't like cocky pregnant women who assumed they'd sail through labor with nothing more than the "hee-hee *WHOOOO*" breathing of Lamaze to ease their "discomfort."

So when first-timers of ours tried to get cocky in the office—say, when they were four weeks from the due date and the reality of what was coming had begun to wash over them—we begged them to be flexible.

"So you're hoping to deliver in the Birthing Center?" I had asked Laura at her 35-week visit.

"Oh, no," Laura said defiantly.

I put down my pen and looked at her, puzzled.

"I *am* delivering in the Birthing Center."

You fool! I wanted to scream. *Take it back right now!*

It was too late. The Labor gods had heard her arrogant, presumptuous statement, and were already cooking up a hellacious experience for poor unsuspecting Laura.

"That's great," I told her. "I'm glad you're so committed. But we urge our patients to remain flexible. Many first labors are more difficult than you ever imagined possible."

"I can handle it," Laura said. "I'm using hyp-nobirthing. Our doula is awesome."

A doula, in the context in which Laura used the term, is a professional labor support person. A doula can and should be a wonderful, energizing, positive presence during labor.

I had heard about hypnobirthing. In fact, I had seen a special about it on "20/20" a year or so be-fore—but none of our patients had tried it yet. It was supposed to allow the woman to labor with-out conventional pain medication because she had been pre-trained in "natural relaxation tech-niques."

"Laura, you're just three centimeters dilated. The cervix is thick and the baby's head is still pretty high," I said. "It's a little early still. Why don't you go home and rest and come back when the contractions are a little more regular?"

"A little more regular? *A little more regular?* I've been in—in *contractions* for three days now! I haven't slept in 48 hours! How much more regu-lar are they going to get? I mean—" here Laura shot a look at the doula, whose name I had yet to learn—*"is it going to get worse than this?"*

Somewhere in their dank, sulphurous cave, the labor gods were snickering behind their hands. I felt sorry for Laura. Her disappointment was raw and palpable.

"I can't believe she talked you into admitting her to the Birthing Center at only 3 cms," Susan, my colleague, said sleepily. I had retreated to the office for a telephonic second opinion.

"Well, I told her she absolutely can't get in the Jacuzzi yet, because that would completely kill her labor," I said. "I can't believe I did this."

"Yeah, you were the one who said, 'over my dead body is anybody getting admitted to the Birthing Center in early labor.' You said it! Remember? You said 'the Birthing Center is for *active labor.*'"

"But what choice did I have? She refused my offer of Pitocin and epidural and she flat-out refused to go home. I told her we were going to treat her as if she were out walking—we weren't going to monitor her or anything, and she had to keep walking. Right now it's only the walking that's keeping the uterus going. When she lies down, the contractions absolutely stop."

"Well, good luck," Susan said. "I'm going back to bed."

Laura was lying on the queen-size bed in a fetal position when I returned to the Birthing Center. Nameless Doula and Jimmy were hovering over her, rubbing various body parts and murmuring, their voices artificially high and squeaky with positivity, like Mister Rogers. I sat on the "birthing ball," a large, squishy latex ball designed for sitting, bouncing and rolling on the floor while in labor, and timed her contractions.

"Laura, the contractions are about nine minutes apart now. The labor is slowing down. Here is my suggestion: we go down to Labor & Delivery and give you some Pitocin and some IV narcotic. You can sleep for a while and we can get you into a more effective contraction pattern."

"Ummmmm —excuse me," Nameless Doula whispered, patting my arm urgently. "Can I talk to you outside?"

"Uh… her birth plan mentions that she doesn't want to be offered pain medication," N.D. said accusingly in the hall outside the birthing room.

"Does her birth plan mention a cesarean?" I snapped at N.D. "Because that's where we're headed if she doesn't accept Pitocin now. I mean it. It's not a good idea to prolong the labor any more."

"Please don't tell her that," N.D. begged. "You'll frighten her."

"Listen, Laura is an adult. She's also my patient," I pointed out. "I've known her for her entire pregnancy. I'm not going to pretend that everything's normal. It's my job to recognize when something is not normal, and to intervene. That's what Laura hired me for."

"To *intervene?*" N.D.'s face registered horror, as though she had just witnessed some godawful massacre.

"No. She hired me for my expertise. She's still in early labor, she's exhausted, and she insisted on being admitted to the hospital. Therefore, I am obliged to intervene. If she wanted to do this at home, it'd be fine. But she can't spend the next fourteen hours in the hospital contracting every nine minutes. [Okay, I was exaggerating a little bit.] The hospital is for active, progressive labor."

"I'm acting as her advocate," N.D. said. "You can talk to her through me."

"No, that won't work," I said. "Laura is my patient. We respect and trust each other. She doesn't need an advocate. *I am one of the good guys.* I will do my talking directly to her."

"I don't want Pitocin!" Laura sobbed, sitting up in the giant bed in her flannel nightshirt. "The Pitocin hurts more than natural labor!"

Here we go again.

"Laura, the reason you can handle these 'natural' contractions is because *they're not doing anything.* They're not dilating your cervix or making the head descend. Do you understand? It's a dysfunctional labor. You need stronger and more frequent contractions—the ones that will move the labor along. You're exhausted, your uterus is exhausted, and it's not good for the baby either, to contract for three days without progress. Don't you want to have the baby?"

"But I wanted to have it in the Birthing Center!"

I didn't understand it. How could so many adult women, who must have gotten used to life's disappointments by the time they decided to bear children, count so exclusively on only one scenario for something as unpredictable as labor? How could they not accept that this powerful thing—

labor—was completely out of their hands? How could they be disappointed when the labor didn't go according to the birth plan, as if you could actually plan something like this?

And why did I have to be the one to tell them the bad news?

"Can't we try an enema? Or nipple stimulation?" Jen (the doula's name was Jen) asked.

"An enema could take hours before the prostaglandins released by the bowel would affect the uterus. You can try nipple stimulation—let's give that an hour or so—and see if you get into a good contraction pattern. But you've got to have regular, strong contractions to have this baby."

Nipple stimulation—literally, the pulling and squeezing of the laboring woman's nipples—works by stimulating the pituitary gland to produce oxytocin (the body's natural Pitocin). When a recently delivered woman breastfeeds her baby, nursing also effects this response, causing the uterus to contract, expel its leftover blood, and return to its original size faster. Nipple stimulation sometimes worked fairly well in women who'd already had a baby, but in exhausted first-timers like Laura, you could practically rub the nipples off and still not achieve good contractions.

Also, with nipple stimulation, you had to keep doing it or it didn't work. A sentient being who instinctively avoids pain is appropriately reluctant to keep doing something known to cause pain.

This usually results in the midwife nagging the patient incessantly.

"Keep doing the nipple stimulation, Laura," I said. "It seems to be doing something." I was standing in the doorway. The smell of lavender was everywhere. It seemed to emanate from Jen's very pores. I hated lavender.

"I will. I just need to rest now."

"Laura, I'm sorry to nag. This nipple stimulation is the only thing standing between you and Pitocin. If you don't do it, we're back in the same situation as before."

I felt like someone's stern, mean-spirited mother, telling her she couldn't go to sleepaway camp with the other kids. I hated playing this role. Why did it have to be like this?

"Uh, Sarah?" Jen stood up. "Can I talk to you outside?"

"I don't think all this negativity is good for her," Jen said, her mouth tensed, her upper teeth showing a little. "I mean—it just feels like you don't have any faith in this labor." She rocked back and forth on her heels.

"That would be because I don't have any faith in this labor," I said harshly. "That is not a reason to judge my character. Laura hired me for my expertise. My expertise tells me this labor has gone sour, and if we ignore that, we imperil her chances of a vaginal delivery. Get it?"

Hypnobitch, I wanted to say, *what are* you *doing about it?*

I mean, really! I'm the midwife, for God's sake! I'm the good guy! Why does there always have to be a bad guy? And why does it have to be me?

Finally I shooed Jen and Jimmy from the room, turned the lights down and settled Laura in the huge bed on her side. I massaged her lower back with a hot compress. It was just us and the pervasive smell of lavender.

"Laura," I began, "I'm sorry you're suffering. I'm sorry you're disappointed. I need to know what you want. No bullshit, no one else speaking for you, no birth plan. What can I do to help you?"

Laura spoke so faintly I could barely hear.

"I need to sleep."

"I know you do."

"Can I just sleep and have contractions anyway?"

"The only way you can do that is if you get an epidural and we give you Pitocin after you're comfortable."

"Then can we please do that?"

Yes, yes, yes! How hard was it for her to say that?

"I'm bailing out," Laura told Jimmy and Jen flatly. "I'm going to Labor & Delivery for an epidural and Pitocin."

Bailing out. There was so much self-judgment attached to this decision.

Jen shot me a fuzzy glare. I ignored her and began collecting the various items of Laura's and Jimmy's that were scattered about. The nurse,

Connie, went ahead to prepare a room for us in Labor & Delivery.

"This is so wonderful," Laura said. "I love this!" She sat up in the bed in the labor room, her head cocked to one side, cocooned in hospital blankets, and pretended to be conducting a symphony. "I hear angels singing!" She giggled and settled back down. Soon she was snoring.

I turned the lights down and tiptoed out. Jen was no longer speaking to anyone. Someone had let the air out of her bicycle tires; someone had peed in her suitcase; someone had killed her houseplants while she was out of town. She was inconsolable.

Three hours later, Laura woke up abruptly and announced, "I have to take a shit!"

Fully dilated.

Jen came back to life a little during the pushing stage.

"Push physiologically!" she admonished Laura. "Breathe as you push!"

"Which way do you think is better, Sarah?" Laura asked.

"I think you should push how your body tells you to push," I answered.

"I like the holding-my-breath thing," Laura said emphatically.

"Sarah, you were right about everything," Laura said as I was leaving. "I can't thank you enough."

It was 6 a.m. and birds were starting to sing outside the window. Jimmy sat in the rocking chair holding their baby boy, Jimmy Jr., singing cowboy songs. Jen had skulked out a while before.

"You don't have to say that, Laura," I said. "It's your first baby. Labor is very difficult sometimes. It's hard to know the right thing to do. I'm sorry you didn't get what you wanted."

"But I did get what I wanted. You were 100 percent right. It didn't matter whether I delivered in the Birthing Center or not. What mattered was getting on with the labor."

Does anyone really mind being told she is 100 percent right once in a while?

Lucien

"Mezanmi! Mezanmi! Why, why, why, why, why, why, why? Jesu, Jesu, Jesu,
Jesu! Why, why, why-why-why-why-why?"

Martine thrashed in the bed. It was hot in the room. The air-conditioning in the hospital was not fully functional, although it was early September, one of the hottest months in New York's protracted summers.

It was 10:48 p.m.

"Martine, you're still five centimeters. It's been almost two hours. Why don't we start some Pitocin and get you an epidural so you can relax?"

"I fear the epidural!"

"I know it sounds scary. But we do a million a day—it's safe, and you really need it. You need to relax and have some good contractions to make progress. Please trust me. "

I was aware of being so tired that I wanted to vomit. I had not been sleeping well.

"I want to take a shower first. Can I take a shower?"

The nurse had a look of concern on her face when she came to the nurses' station. I had my head down on the desk, wishing I were anywhere but there.

"I can't get the FH." [Fetal heart rate]

"What do you mean, you can't get the FH?" I snapped at her. "It was fine before she took a shower."

"I know, but now I can't find it."

Martine was my private patient. She was a friend and parishioner of the man who had taught me Creole, Pasté Louis, who was the pastor of Frantz' church in Flatbush, Brooklyn. She had transferred to our practice, on his advice, from a doctor at Mt. Zion Medical Center. I had developed a reputation in the Haitian community around the Heights Medical Center. I was "the white midwife who spoke Creole."

I had followed Martine since she was eighteen weeks pregnant. Ironically, she was the first patient I saw in the office when I came back from Haiti. She helped me practice Creole, she brought me homemade plantain chips, and she called me at home sometimes at night to chat.

Martine had a nineteen-year-old daughter. She and her husband had been unable to have any more children, despite years of trying and many miscarriages. Long after they had given up, Martine had gotten pregnant unexpectedly. Just before she found out she was pregnant, her husband was killed in a drive-by shooting. He had been standing outside of a Haitian nightclub near their apartment.

Martine was 38 years old. She did not blame anyone else for her troubles.

"Give me more goo." The nurse squeezed a dollop of gel onto Martine's belly.

There was a terrible silence in Martine's belly. I got the feeling I used to get in the clinic when a patient would tell me the baby had not moved for a day or two. When I put the miniature ultrasound device—the "doptone"—onto the belly, I could sometimes tell right away. If it was really quiet in there, I knew it was going to be bad, and the nausea crept in, starting at the bottom of my stomach and working its way up to my throat, making a bitter, metallic taste in the back of my mouth.

Martine had been on the monitor for hours, without so much as a tiny, insignificant dip in the heart rate.

Good babies don't go bad in labor.

"Give me an internal."

"What is that?" Martine was scared.

"I need to monitor the baby's heart rate with an internal monitor. It goes on the baby's scalp."

"Why do you have to do that?"

I felt the blind panic I feel when facing too many tasks at once. I have to reassure this woman, whom I love, explaining calmly in lay terms why I am doing these things, all the while trying to screw a spiral electrode onto the baby's scalp through her cervix. I used to fantasize that I had a bulb on my head that lit up when I was overloaded. The patient, observing this light, would immediately stop asking questions. The light meant: *Overload. Can't talk now. Will explain later.*

Good babies don't go bad in labor.

That was what Marjorie told us day after day in midwifery school.

That's why we're able to come back to work day after day. Because we know that good babies who are tolerating labor will not suddenly die.

So where was the FH?

"This scalp electrode isn't working! Get me another one!" I snapped at the nurse.

"I'm getting Dr. Halpern."

Mark Halpern, my friend and colleague, was the obstetrical consultant for our practice. That meant he was the guy who did our c-sections for us, the guy who consulted on our patients when they developed problems during pregnancy, the guy we talked to before inducing someone's labor or giving someone an epidural. He was "in house" that night—one of his own patients was in labor as well.

He appeared in the doorway, struggling to roll the portable sonogram machine into Martine's room. Mark was great, he liked us, our patients loved him, but he didn't like conflict or bad news or being awakened in the middle of the night.

He eyeballed the paper tracing hanging from the fetal monitor.

"There can't be anything wrong," he said calmly. "Not with that tracing."

You see? Good babies don't go bad.

"What is it? What's wrong?" Martine was panicked.

"We're just doing a sonogram to locate the baby's heart so we can monitor him."

Mark, normally chatty and reassuring with patients, said nothing as he stroked the sonographic transducer back and forth across Martine's belly. I peered frantically at the screen. I rubbed my eyes. I was so tired. I felt that same sour taste welling up in my throat for the millionth time.

I hate my job.

Still Mark said nothing. He set the machine to M-mode.

But that couldn't be right. M-mode was what they used to diagnose fetal death in utero. It showed the heart muscle's activity over time. A wavy pattern meant the heart muscle was still alive, still fluttering, still receiving electrical impulses. A flat pattern meant—

Martine started to whimper.

"What is it? How is my baby? How is Lucien?"

"Mark, please," I begged him. "Say something."

Mark looked acutely uncomfortable. His face turned red.

"It's the damnedest thing. I can't figure it out," he mumbled, staring at the screen.

"What is it?"

"It seems the baby has died. I'm so sorry. I can't understand it."

Good babies don't go bad in labor. They don't. They can't. Because if they can, then we cannot come to work any more.

I cannot come to work any more. I cannot do anything any more.

Martine screamed: "*Jesu, Jesu, Jesu!*"

Two days, later, walking out of the hospital in the dark, I am having a waking dream.

I see Lucien before me, only now he is a two-year-old. He has Martine's long, thin face and pointed chin. He still has big ears—the ears I stroked lightly with my fingertip as his newborn body lay under the warmer in the Operating Room. His eyes then were wide open, his pupils completely expanded. Now his eyes are narrowed, squinty, staring at me accusingly.

Lucien is angry with me. *Li fache.*

Why did I let him die? Why didn't I protect him?

He shakes his fist at me. He is shouting at me in toddler's Creole. I can't understand what he is saying. He is so angry.

I want to live! He says. *M'vle viv!*

I shake my head to rid myself of the vision.

"Sarah, you didn't kill that baby," Moe says. "You've got to get a grip."

We are sitting in a Caribbean bar in the East Village. We have ordered conch fritters and coconut shrimp, which taste like cardboard and styrofoam in my mouth. It takes so much effort to chew this food. There is a paper umbrella in my glass, and a swizzle stick in the shape of a monkey. It's just like being on the beach in the Caribbean. Except that I am in Manhattan, it is September, my last vacation is a distant memory, and I don't want to go back to work again. Ever. I don't want to do anything again. I certainly don't want to go on vacation again.

I can never go on vacation again. I can never lie on a beach again, drinking out of a coconut with a sandy beach towel wrapped around my legs. I killed a baby.

"Sarah, are you listening to me?"

"Se pa fót ou," Martine said. (It is not your fault.)

We were sitting on the edge of her bed in her postpartum room. She was getting ready to go home. After all of that, she couldn't push the baby out and Mark had to do a cesarean. A cesarean for a baby that was dead.

"Sarah, *m'pa kondane ou. Se pa fót ou!"* (I don't blame you. It is not your fault!)

"Why can't you blame me?" I say in English. I have no Creole left.

"*Paske se pa fót ou. Bondye bon. Ti bébé-a, li pat ka viv.*" (Because it is not your fault. God is good. The baby could not live.)

"God is *not* good. Why couldn't the baby live?"

"*Sarah, genyen okenn bagay ke nou pa ka konprann.*" (There are some things that we cannot understand.)

"Please blame me! *Please.* I didn't protect him. Why can't you just blame me? Don't you need a reason? *Just blame me!*"

"*Sarah, pa gen razon toujou.*" (There is not always a reason.) "*F'ok ou padonne tèt ou.*" (You must forgive yourself.)

"Sarah, listen. You can't keep not talking about this."

Susan, my boss, is telling me I need to get a psychiatric evaluation. Everybody at work is "talking about me."

Bad enough I killed a baby. Now everyone thinks I'm crazy.

"Are you sleeping at all?"

"That's all I do right now. Sleep, sleep, sleep."

"Are you taking something to sleep?"

"Just Benadryl."

"Benadryl's no good! It suppresses REM sleep."

"That's good. I don't have the energy to dream anyway."

"Sarah, I want you to go see my therapist. She's great with bereavement issues. She can help you."

"I don't want to see someone who's 'great with bereavement issues'! I just want to be left alone! I'm fine."

"Sarah, you're not fine. Dr. Russo is very worried about you."

"Dr. Russo? That big blowhard? He doesn't even like me. It's none of his business, anyway."

"He says you look like you are crying all the time. He says you seem very tired. All the nurses say you are angry, and you look as though you are falling asleep all the time, and sometimes you slam around the nurses' station, and you barely act civil to anyone."

"That's not true!"

I work like a fucking dog and they can't ever cut me a break, even now. I killed a baby, and I still have to go to work. How the hell am I supposed to act?

"Well, I never complain about them, even when they are nasty or make unsolicited comments about things they know nothing about. Why do they have to complain about me? Why can't they mind their own business?"

"They're not complaining, Sarah. They're worried about you. They love you. Sarah, I want you to take a leave of absence."

"I can't afford it. Besides, what would I do?"

"A paid leave of absence. A couple of weeks only. Get intensive therapy, go to Jamaica, do yoga, meditate, get acupuncture, go to the gym, shoot hoops—do whatever you want. But you need to regroup and think this through. You did not kill that baby. You have to accept that. And you can't come back to work until you're better. In fact, I want a therapist to say that you're better. In writing."

"I don't think this is fair! If I didn't kill that baby, as you and everybody else are saying, then what have I done wrong? Nothing! Have I compromised patient care? Have I behaved inappropriately? No. I've done nothing. So why am I being punished?"

"Don't think of it as punishment. Think of it as a paid holiday."

"A psychiatric leave of absence? *Great!* Thanks a lot!"

So I gave in. I took an enforced leave of absence, with pay. I saw Susan's therapist, Dr. Singer, who was, indeed, great with bereavement issues.

"I'm curious as to why you think you killed the fetus. Terrible things happen in your profession—you said it yourself—usually for no reason at all. You know this. Why is this your sole responsibility?"

I'm lying on the couch in Dr. Singer's office. It's dark. I just want to sleep a little while—I am so tired!—but she keeps asking me the same questions over and over.

"What makes you say you killed the fetus?"

Leave me alone, leave me alone, leave me alone.

"What makes you so powerful?" Dr. Singer asked.

"What do you mean by that?"

"You said you didn't protect the fetus. What makes you think you have so much power that you can prevent death?"

"Because good babies don't die in labor. That's why. He was a good baby. He shouldn't have died. I should have stopped it. "

"It's clear that this was not a 'good baby,' Sarah, for whatever reason. What I'm trying to get at is your image of yourself. Do you actually believe that you are so powerful you can prevent an accidental death in utero?"

"I saved a baby's life once. Her name is Lucia Guarnaccia. She wasn't breathing, and I resuscitated her. It was when I was a new nurse. I felt good about that this whole time until now."

"You should keep feeling good about that. It's great that you saved her life. Her life was meant to be saved. But this fetus was not a 'good baby,' no matter what you say, or he wouldn't have died. Let's talk about why you think you have so much power."

Let's talk about it, let's talk about it, let's talk about it.

I took yoga at the Integral Yoga Institute—the 3:30 beginner Hatha class—every day for a week. The rooms were dark and warm. The air smelled damply of orange and bergamot. At the end of "deep relaxation," the instructor rang Tibetan chimes to bring us back. I slept lightly during deep relaxation and sobbed quietly during the chanting and the inversions. When I did *sarvan-gaasaana*—shoulder stand—tears pooled in my ears. On the second day, the instructor brought a box of generic tissues to my mat and left it there. Once, an instructor squeezed my hand at the end of class without speaking.

On the fifth day, during deep relaxation, I saw Lucien again. This time he was a fetus, slowly asphyxiating inside Martine's womb, struggling and fighting, his little fists balled up, thrashing, squirming, arching his back.

I opened my eyes wide. The vision persisted. I rubbed my face roughly. I was starting to cry, great racking sobs that tore through me violently. The person on the mat next to mine was snoring gently.

Just go through it; go through it, my voice told me. I lay back and closed my eyes again, breathing shakily through my mouth. Now Lucien was quieter. A calm entered his body. As he ceased struggling, he gazed at me and smiled beatifical-ly. *I forgive you, Sarah*, he seemed to say. *Can you forgive yourself?*

Dear Sarah

Dear Sarah:

Manning is three months old now, and I finally have some time to do things I have meant to do for a very long time. I must say, though, he keeps me running!

How can I begin to thank you for the patience, kindness, expertise and love you showed me during my pregnancy and labor? I want you to know that I am completely satisfied with my experience, and would do it all over again in the exact same way if I had to (well, maybe without the stitches!).

You and Maureen and Susan are performing a tremendous service for the women of Brooklyn. Throughout my pregnancy and labor I felt safe, secure and loved.

I will never forget you.

Love,
Hilda H.

Dear Sarah Porter:

Thank you so much for taking such loving care of me and for delivering my beautiful daughter Marguerite. Without you I couldn't have done it.

Wishing you a beautiful year and many happy deliveries.

Sincerely,

Sophia W.

I think of Sophia's labor, how she pushed and pushed and pushed and we were ready to call a c-section and she said, "Don't give up on me, Sarah." And she pushed a little more and out came Marguerite, eight pounds thirteen ounces, head misshapen like a bruised fruit, and I put her on Sophia's belly and she sobbed and sobbed and sobbed.

I hear the words of Natalie, one of the night nurses, when I said I wanted to get the hell out of midwifery—*But Sarah, you have a gift.*

You have a gift, Sarah.

But I need a job that hurts me less.

Then I think of that first-grader, Desireé, whose mother came to Labor & Delivery repeatedly to find me after six years, and who, when she spotted me, whispered to Desireé, who ran to me without fear or shyness or self-consciousness and jumped at me and held me around the waist, and I am pretty sure Desireé was the slimy little baby I'm holding up in the photograph—the one where I look so sweaty and happy. I think that was Desireé.

I read and re-read those letters, and I study the photographs my patients send me. Sometimes the last name of the baby is different from the mother's last name, and I struggle to recall the circumstances and the mother's last name to place the baby in a context, a living memory.

Do I have a gift?

Sometimes, like today, I look into the eyes of a neurologically damaged 16-year-old girl, nothing but sweetness in her, who is pregnant as a result of nonconsensual intercourse with a 24-year-old man named Omar who lives in her apartment building, a girl whose facial features most resemble Fetal Alcohol Syndrome, but whose exact neurologic deficits cannot be defined, whose mother died of AIDS five years ago, whose aunts have assumed responsibility for her care, whose labor has been going on for the past 24 hours, who merely needs someone to look into her eyes and tell her, tacitly or overtly, "We are going to take care of you."

I look into that girl's eyes and her hand reaches for me involuntarily when a contraction overtakes her, and I put down my pen and the chart and the all-important documentation (*Your Honor! She concealed the pregnancy until she was 32 weeks along! She had only two prenatal visits! She could not tolerate vaginal exams and failed to show up for her diabetes test! I am not responsible for what came out of her!*), and I take her hand. And we just sit there, me and that girl, eyes locked, and we hold hands for a few minutes, until someone comes in to ask me to do something else, some other task.

And in those moments, I hear myself say, *"You are meant to do this."*

And maybe I am right.

And some other times, I teach a medical student how to tie surgical knots or start an IV, or I let the student deliver a baby with me, and it doesn't cost me anything, and the medical student's whole 24-hour call is redeemed.

And sometimes I can make a patient feel safe just by patting her arm or admiring her fetus' beautiful profile on the sonogram, or saying, *"This is supposed to happen. This is normal."* I feel a great surge of joy sometimes.

How lucky can you get?

Other times, when I am at a patient's bedside at 4 a.m., and we are entering the third hour of pushing, and my attending physician is home in bed, having made it clear that he does not wish to be called unless there is an immediate need for a c-section, and every time the fetal heart rate decelerates to the 60s from its normal baseline of 150 I feel a wave of nausea that is rooted in both apprehension and exhaustion.

Why do I have to do this? I don't need this.

Dear Sarah:

Words cannot express how fortunate I am to have found you. One of the most precious gifts on earth is the gift of Life. I feel blessed that you were part of my experience. I promise to tell Jeremy and Julian about the kind and caring woman who helped me through both my pregnancies and labors. You will always be in my heart.

Love,

Carla K.

"What does it mean to you, when your patients say these things?" (Dr. Singer)

"What do you mean?"

By now, my sessions with Dr. Singer seemed to consist entirely of her asking me questions about my self-image, and me asking her what she meant.

"I mean, how important is it for you to feel powerful? Essential?"

"I've never given it much thought. The patients sometimes say things like, 'I couldn't have done it without you,' and even though it's flattering, I know it's not strictly true. Besides, they don't know about Lucien."

"What do you mean, 'they don't know about Lucien?'"

"They don't know I killed a baby."

"Sarah. You didn't kill that fetus. You are a gifted midwife who cares about her patients very much. Your care and concern make a difference in their lives. Why can't you accept that? Why can't you find happiness in that?"

"Because I can't stop thinking about Lucien. Besides, those patients *could* have done it without me. They just think they couldn't have. I'm extraneous."

"I don't believe that and neither do you. Instead of punishing yourself constantly, why don't you ask yourself why you chose this profession. Let's explore what it means to you to be in a career where you are constantly *essential* to people."

Let's explore, let's explore, let's explore.

Williamsburg

The northbound M and J trains make their slow, huffing way to Jamaica, Queens, by way of Williamsburg, Brooklyn. Without warning, just after Essex Street in Manhattan, the train bursts above ground, like a swimmer saved from drowning, gasping for air as he breaks the surface. The train is instantaneously flooded with light, squeaking along at treetop level, revealing in its windows the upper floors of red-brick brownstones, housing projects and small factories housed in grim, gray limestone buildings.

As the train traverses the Williamsburg Bridge with a determined clackety-clack, the gunmetal-gray water of the East River sprawling below, the tallest buildings you see are five and six stories high. Only the smokestack of the Domino Sugar factory disrupts the humble skyline.

A large, brazen sign greets you if you care to scan the ground below and to your right.

"Welcome to Brooklyn. You Name It, We Got It." The names of the (former) Brooklyn borough president and the (former) mayor are stenciled neatly at the bottom.

The girders that support the pedestrian walkway are painted bubble-gum pink. Below, to the south of the elevated tracks, are row houses and narrow, teeming streets. The street cleaners don't get here often.

The lowlights of Williamsburg stand in humble apposition to the Manhattan skyline across the water. Everything that is arrogant, presumptuous, worshipful of commerce—that is, the lower Manhattan skyline—is mocked by the stubborn, four-story humility of Williamsburg. Even the business establishments are modest and last-century: The Dandy Zipper Mfr., the Magrill Brothers, the Gretsch Building No. 4.

The corner of Marcy Avenue and Broadway offers a gaudy array of modest retail establishments: Dora's Beauty Palace. Chick'in 'n Biskit. 99-cent Dream. Esayi Health and Beauty. ("*Designer* fragrances!"). LB Grocery ("butterolls and coffee"). Ace Variety. Rainbow Ladies Sportswear. La Borinquena. Bargain Bazaar. Marvel Pharmacy. These stores do not pretend—they do not even try—to be modern. The lighting, the window panes, the very scents that emanate from them are last-millenium.

At the corner of Marcy Ave. and Broadway a large, 8-story red-brick official-looking building looms—certainly the tallest of its kind here. A sign heralds its "CONTENTS: New York City Human Resources Administration. North Brooklyn Food Stamp Center. The church of JESUS CHRIST of Latter-Day Saints."

All in one building!

I loved Williamsburg.

If you walk down Marcy Ave. to Division Ave., past the housing projects, the traffic on the Belt Parkway humming steadily below and to your left, you experience a kind of border crossing. Division Avenue almost literally divides the Satmar Hasidic Jewish residents from the Latino ones. There's a gray belt, a mixture, in the few blocks on either side of the Avenue, but if you keep walking, you enter another dimension.

The *Payess* Zone.

Payess are the long, tubular sidelocks worn by Satmar Hasidic men, in keeping with the Biblical injunction against cutting facial hair. *Payess* are an easy way to distinguish Satmar Hasidim from other Hasidic sects that do not consider sidelocks facial hair, and therefore cut them.

Urban legends notwithstanding, Hasidic Jewish couples do not have sex through a hole in the sheet. Hasidic couples are *supposed* to have good sex, they are *entitled* to have good sex, and failure to get good sex is a legitimate reason for an Hasidic wife to get a *get* (a Jewish divorce). Unfortunately, many Hasidic women do not really *get* this.

RabbiHeimanwarnedmeaboutthisinourtwo-hour tete-à-tete at Starbucks on Atlantic Avenue. We were trying to break into Williamsburg. My hospital, the Heights Medical Center, had rented space in a basement office there—and the Rabbi had kindly agreed to guide me.

"It's a tough nut to crack," he said sympathetically. "You must advertise, of course, but beyond that, you must be patient. These women are slow to accept change. Your office is new, no?"

I had to admit it was. We had only been coming there for two months. Other medical centers in Brooklyn had reached out to the Satmar population decades ago. Our mission was to attract a significant portion of this healthy, fertile, child-bearing population to our hospital.

"Well, Rabbi," I said, hoping I didn't have lipstick on my teeth, "as midwives, we have a lot to offer these women. We're very sensitive to their needs, we give a very personalized brand of care and we're anxious to do our part to educate these women about their health."

"It is good that you are doing this," Rabbi Heiman said solemnly, sipping from a *grande* cup of chai latte. "The women of this community need more choices."

He was a rotund man of about five-foot-eight, a darling man—sweet, funny, brilliant, with eyes the color of Windex. Unlike many Hasidic men I had met before, he truly looked a woman in the eye. Although Jewish law prohibits men from touching women other than their wives, Rabbi

Heiman and I experienced a virtual handshake. Throughout our conversation he eyed me steadily, unflinchingly, watching my reactions and smiling enthusiastically at times.

"Their needs for health education are enormous. They don't know about breast self-exam, for example, and they don't go for mammograms unless they find something. They don't get Pap smears regularly unless they're pregnant. They don't know anything about the menopause. They don't really learn much about sex before they are married, and a great many of them don't experience any sexual enjoyment at all. You can bring this up, but not immediately. You must wait until the woman brings it up in conversation. You must earn their trust."

"Of course, Rabbi. But—I—I wonder— how frank can I be with them?"

"You mean about sex? Once they trust you, you can say almost anything."

I learned a lot from Rabbi Heiman. For example, although the 613 *mitzvot* (the positive and negative commandments handed down in the Torah) forbade a man from touching his wife for seven days after she finishes her menstrual period, which comes from the uterus, bleeding from the vagina is not considered *tamay* (impure). But many Hasidic Jewish women were afraid of any blood from "down there."

My first Hasidic patient at our Williamsburg office came directly from Rabbi Heiman himself.

She was his cousin's sister-in-law, Nechama, and she had a problem.

Nechama and her husband, Shmuel, entered the office with a flourish. It was cold for November, and the two of them wore what seemed to be a stack of coats apiece. Merely removing their outer garments took a decent amount of time.

They finally sat. A few moments of silence passed. I remembered Rabbi Heiman's words of advice:

"Silence is golden. Be patient, and let the woman bring up what is on her mind."

I smiled at Nechama and her man. He was cut from the Rabbi Heiman cloth, choosing to look me squarely in the eye. Another minute ticked by.

"So how can I help you today?"

Nechama sneaked a look at her husband and fixed her eyes on the paperweight near the edge of the desk—someone's cast-off *"Recuerdo de Cancun"*—a glass globe depicting a mermaid coming out of a cave under the sea. She began all in a rush:

"I have a severe problem. When my husband tries to have—relationships with me, it hurts." She paused, overwhelmed.

"It hurts when?" I asked.

"When he is going inside me. It hurts very badly."

Ah, *pain on intromission*! How often did an ex-journalist like me get to use that lilting phrase? I'd probably used it only once or twice before in my lifetime.

intromission (in"tro-mish'un) the entrance
of one part or object into another

vs. **intermission** (in'ter'mish'un)
an interval between the parts of an
entertainment (as the acts of a play)

Nechama and Shmuel continued to stare at me.

"So you have been unable to complete the act of intercourse?"

"Yes."

"You have never been able to have relations?"

"No."

"You have tried many times?"

"Yes. Since we got married in July. It is a very bad problem."

This couple had been trying unsuccessfully since *July* to have sex!

Rabbi Heiman must have really had faith in me, to send me this poor woman with this terrible problem. I was determined not to let him down.

"Well, this *is* a problem. You are a married couple, you are supposed to be enjoying each other. Also you may want to have children soon. Let me examine Nechama in the exam room, and then we will see. It is possible that you have an actual physical problem, but more likely it is a lesser problem that can be fixed without too much difficulty."

Nechama flinched as I tried to insert a small speculum.

"That's it! That's where it hurts!"

There was no obstruction that I could see.

"Let me try to place it a little bit more. Relax your muscles deeply. Breathe in and out."

The speculum went in the rest of the way.

"Wow, Nechama, this is great. You did very well. Now let me try to examine you with two fingers."

I saw fresh blood coming from her vagina as I attempted to examine her. Her *hymen*—as distinguished from Rabbi *Heiman*, her cousin-in-law—was shredded and bleeding a little.

> **Hymen** (hi´men) the membranous fold partly or completely closing the vaginal orifice. Adj., **hy´menal**.

Nechama's problem was—or had been—that she had possessed an intact hymen! No wonder her husband couldn't "have relationships" with her! But now it was gone! I, Sarah Porter, had broken Nechama's hymen!

Men! Send me your virgins! I will deflower them! I am all-powerful!

What would Dr. Singer say?

We tried again with a larger speculum. This time I let Nechama insert it. It worked! Nechama was no longer a virgin and now she could have "relationships" with her cute man.

I was ecstatic. I blotted the blood from the shreds of Nechama's hymen, sat her up, and went to the waiting room to call Shmuel back into the office.

"Nechama's problem was simple to diagnose and easy to solve. She had an intact hymen—that's a thin membrane of tissue, like a wall, that covers the vagina inside. I was able to insert a small speculum and the hymen gave way. Then Nechama was able to insert a larger speculum herself," I said enthusiastically.

"So? This is good, yes?"

"Good? This is *great!*"

Nechama entered the room, blushing like a bride on her wedding night. This was to be her wedding night! I felt like following them back to their apartment, putting on some Kenny G. CDs, lighting aromatherapy candles, and giving them specific instructions:

See that right there? Touch that.

Now touch that.

"You saw blood, no?"

"Oh, yes. There was blood from the hymen. But it's not coming from above so it's not impure. It's okay for you to have sex today if you want to."

Nechama looked doubtful.

"You're sure?"

"I'm absolutely positive. But if you want to wait until it stops and do the whole *mikvah* thing, you can."

[The *mikvah* was the ritual bath that Orthodox women immersed themselves in each month exactly eight days after the last of their menstrual blood. This assured "cleanliness," and meant they were good to go.]

"It's just that you might get your menses soon after that and would have to wait even longer. You've been waiting since July to have relations. You're certainly entitled to start now. It's not the impure blood, I promise you."

I gave Nechama a plastic speculum and tons of samples of Astroglide, a vaginal lubricant. I told her to keep practicing with the speculum, but to practice with Shmuel as well.

They were beaming.

"We can't thank you enough," Shmuel said, again meeting my eyes firmly.

"Yes you can," I said. "Tell your friends about this place, and have your first baby with us."

I loved Williamsburg.

The Infidelity Clinic

In a healthy human male, a single ejaculate contains between 125 million and 600 million sperm. When the sperm count is below 120 million, the man is considered sterile. Imagine that! Less than 120 million sperm per shot—*you poor, sterile bastard.*

I got off the exam table, and approximately 400 million sperm trickled down my legs.

I panicked. I tried to calculate the cost of this waste; the price per sperm, if you will. It probably couldn't be calculated in dollars. Perhaps lira—

"Sarah, you're ready to go?"

Dr. Nyall peered into the room again.

"Dr. Nyall—is frozen sperm—does it have more sperm per cc than the average ejaculate?"

She hemmed and hawed for a minute.

"Well, yes, Sarah, it does, but the motility of frozen sperm is not as high-quality as fresh. That's why we put it in a broth to enhance it, and that's why we centrifuge several ejaculates for one insemination."

Great! So I had the equivalent of *several ejaculates* running down my leg.

It was 6:30 a.m. I had arrived at Dr. Nyall's office at five o'clock for the insemination. They wanted you to lie on the table with your legs up for a good twenty minutes afterwards—for good luck? Or to fight gravity? Since I had to work today, I had taken the earliest appointment.

Dr. Nyall's waiting room was packed when I walked out. Hasidic couples, older women—women who looked much older than I—sheepish-looking men. I glanced at the sign-in sheet as I waited to pay my bill. There were already at least thirty names and it was only 6:30 a.m.!

The hormones I was taking to boost my aging ovaries gave me terrible insomnia, night sweats, and what Dr. Nyall called "emotional liability." That meant I felt like crying most of the time, when I wasn't shouting at someone or arguing about things like the caloric content of sushi. I was insufferable.

Moe thought I was crazy. But I wanted to have a baby—just one baby.

I had chosen the most socially unfortunate time of my life to arrive at this conclusion. I had had occasional dates since becoming a midwife, and Frantz and I had definitely gone all the way a few times, but nothing ever panned out. I had been far too occupied during midwifery school to pursue a social life that included men. I no longer met men my own age at work. What had once been a giant pool of potentially available men was now a giant pool of very young men. The men in my age group who worked at my hospital were married or gay or repellent, and I didn't exactly have a wild social life outside of my female friends, most of whom worked with me.

I had run out of sex. I was totally involved in our practice, with almost no free time to pursue a source of live sperm, and I was almost 40 years old.

It's funny how all your ability to attract men seems to vanish when you get to age 40. Moe, who was four years younger than I, had a theory. The Sex-Pool Theory.

"There's a specific amount of sex in the pool, not designated for anyone in particular, and when it gets used up, that's it. No more sex."

"What do you mean?"

"I mean it's like Social Security. It's out there, in a giant pool. As we age, the pool is being rapidly depleted. And when it's all gone, there's no more sex for anybody."

"Moe, that doesn't make any sense."

"Maybe not in concrete terms, but, tell me: Are you having sex? Am I having sex?"

"Well, *you* are."

"Well, yes—but not very often. It's because of all those teenagers who are having sex too early. They're using up all the sex in the pool. *They're taking the sex that should be ours!*"

There was no arguing with Moe when she got like this.

Having used up most of the supply of eligible doctors, first at NYCAS and later at the Heights Medical Center, without achieving a Mrs.M.D. degree, Moe was now dating a Rastafarian bass player. The band, So Jah Say, was based in Brooklyn but traveled all over the East Coast and the West Indies. Moe's bass player, Barrington, was sweet and sexy but he kept giving Moe *trichomonas vaginalis*—a common, easily treated type of sexually transmitted infection.

So here I was, almost 40, and the reproductive part of my life had nearly passed me by. I had spent most of my (probably) fertile thirties using up all my energy, staying up all night, attending to other people's babies. Now I wanted one of my own—just one. Had I waited too long?

"Sarah? It's Dr. Nyall. How are you?"

"Why do you sound like that?"

It was Saturday morning, day five of my period. I had failed my third cycle of intrauterine insemination and was now on deck for in vitro. I had managed to save just enough money to cover one, maybe two cycles of in vitro.

"Sarah, your hormone levels are very bad this month. It would not be wise to do IVF this cycle."

"What?"

"Your FSH is through the roof and your estrogen is no good either."

"What does that mean?"

"It means it would be a waste of time and money to do IVF this month."

"But what does it mean, long-term?"

"Why don't you take a month off and come and see me on day three of your next natural cycle. We'll re-do the hormone assays then."

In case you were wondering—yes, you can buy sperm with a credit card. Before I started my long, desperate, expensive ordeal with Dr. Nyall, I had done a couple of "do-it-yourself" inseminations at home. The credit card bill comes with a discreet reference to "Pvt. Endo Lab."

You go to a private lab—there are many high-quality sperm banks in Manhattan—for the initial evaluation, blood tests, etc. You are given a list of donors to choose from, which you contemplate for a brief period of time.

It felt like the hour or two before a blind date with great prospects. I was all atwitter. How would I ever decide?

To keep them straight in my mind, I gave them nicknames.

"Lars"—Donor No. 4635A—was the one most ethnically like me. Scandinavian on one side, German-Irish on the other.

"A dashing, blond, blue-eyed professional jazz musician, Lars has an undergraduate degree in performance art," Moe announced in her "Oprah" voice.

"Carlos"—Donor No. 7834A—was half-Dominican, half-Puerto Rican. He was 5' 11," average build, a medical student with an undergraduate degree in physics.

" 'Average build,' " Moe said scornfully. "You know what *that* means." She made a limp-pinky sign to indicate a very small penis.

"Rudolph" was fascinating as well. Donor No. 9023A was a "frequent donor" (I wondered if he had accrued bonus miles by now) who had successfully "fathered" three viable babies at last count. Rudolph was six feet tall with brown, thinning hair and blue eyes. Rudolph was a contractor for a large construction company. He had an Associates' Degree in computer studies.

Do powerful sperm trump higher education? These were the choices I faced.

Moe decided to help me. She drew little cartoon figures of Carlos, Rudolph and Lars, as well as "Osgood," her personal fave. Osgood—Donor No. 2345A to you—was very very short but very very smart. Osgood, five feet three inches tall, had two graduate degrees—Spanish literature and Religion—and was a Ph.D. candidate.

Osgood was never even in the running as far as I was concerned, but Moe threw him into the lineup to make it interesting.

"Carlos? Rudolph? Osgood? Lars." She shuffled the four drawings rapidly and began to wave them before me in random fashion.

"Carlos."

"Lars."

"*Os*good!"

"Ruuuuuudolph."

"Rudolph-Osgood-Carlos-Lars. Lars-Osgood-Carlos-Rudolph. Carlos…"

From experience, we knew that some of the cutest babies came from the most exotic ethnic mixes. Iranian-Dominican, for example, or North African-Polish.

We said, as one, "*Carrrrrrr*los!"

In this way it was decided.

Carlos became my steady date. Once a month I went to the lab to pick up my frozen sperm packed in liquid nitrogen. The tank weighed about thirty pounds.

"Wait! Let me get a picture!" Moe ran ahead of me to snap a photo as I crossed the threshold of my apartment lugging Carlos's concupiscent curds [see Wallace Stevens, "The Emperor of Ice Cream."].

" 'Carlos and Sarah—their honeymoon.' Wait! Lemme get one more."

"Did you get the fishtank thermometer?"

We waited patiently until the warm water had brought Carlos up to the ideal temperature.

"Now, assume the position!" Moe instructed me in a deep, stentorian, military voice.

I obediently got on my bed, frog style, with my butt elevated on two pillows. Moe placed the plastic speculum excitedly and wiggled the plastic pipette into it.

"I think I actually got it into your cervix!" she exclaimed. "Does that make me the baby daddy?"

That was when it was still funny, a diversion, a project.

Now, at almost forty, my hormones were acting as though I was eighty. Why me? Everyone in my family was fertile—my mother, my sisters, my aunts. Why did this have to happen to me?

Was there something fundamentally wrong with my character? Was I simply too selfish to have children? Was I being punished for something? Would it be too hard on a kid to have me as a mother?

I tried to figure it out, why I wanted this so much.

"I just want someone to say about me after I'm gone, 'My mother always used to read to me. My mother used to say...' I just want to have been someone's mother," I explained to Moe.

"A rug rat. Eeeeeeyew," Moe said, mock-shivering. "I just don't get it. I don't know if I ever want to have one. Maybe there's something wrong with me."

"I just want to be someone's mother. I want to last more than one generation. I want someone to talk about me after I'm dead."

"I'll talk about you, bitch."

"Slut, what makes you think you'll outlive me?"

"Sarah. It's Doctor Nyall. I'm afraid I don't have very good news. Your Day Three Estriol and FSH are no good."

"Sarah?"

"Sarah? What do you want to do?"

"Can't you boost me?"

"I beg your pardon?"

315

"Can't you boost me? Can't you induce ovulation? I mean, what is the Pergonal and Clomid for if not to jolt my ovaries? I mean, you told me to take a cycle off and I did. And now my hormones are no good. Can't we just start Clomid and Pergonal again and see what happens?"

"I would hate to waste your time, Sarah. And your money."

"It's *my time*! And my money! I'll choose to waste it if I want to!"

"My advice to you is to do nothing this cycle, stop the Pergonal, come back on Day Three of your next cycle and we'll re-evaluate. But I don't think the situation's going to change."

"You just don't want to bring your numbers down! That's what this is about, isn't it?"

I loathed Dr. Nyall—her smugness, her two perfect children, her expensive shoes.

"What do you mean?"

"You're in a relatively new Repro-Endo program, and you can't afford to get bad statistics. If you do an IVF cycle for me, and I fail, it'll pull your numbers down! Isn't that it?"

"Sarah, I'm sorry you're upset."

"I'm not upset!" (*Just because I'm sobbing doesn't mean I'm upset!*)

I was almost out of money. I had been using up the IVF money to pay for the drugs and the office visits, and I would have to charge some of the cycle on my already maxed-out credit card. My fortieth birthday was next month.

I was so tired.

I hated when patients asked me, "Do you have children?" Why wasn't a simple "no" answer sufficient to end that conversation? Why did a "no" often lead to raised eyebrows and a sarcastic, "Why not? Seen too much?" or a vaguely disapproving, "Oh, so you *didn't want to go through this yourself?*" or, flat-out puzzled and disappointed, "Isn't it *weird* for you to be in this profession and not have children?" Even some of the ones who didn't say anything gave me The Look.

"Yes!" I wanted to shout. "Yes! It *is* weird to be in this profession and not have children! Especially when women who take their fertility for granted ask me probing questions about mine!"

Perhaps I'd get a badge, or a hat, or a tattoo or a t-shirt.

"Barren," it would say, or "Failed three IUI's and one IVF," or "Infertile—Don't Ask."

"How does this image of yourself square with your overall self-image?" (Dr. Singer)

"What do you mean?"

"You as an older single parent, superwoman, achieving a pregnancy against difficult odds, struggling with the enormous emotional tasks of parenthood without anyone else in the picture?"

None of your business, none of your business, none of your business.

Dr. Nyall reluctantly agreed to try one more IVF cycle after two months completely off drugs. I had been at it for almost a year, not counting the home inseminations.

I had not realized just how insane the Clomid and Pergonal made me until I was off them for a while. So that's why I cried in the middle of Atlantic Avenue when I saw a dog tied to a parking meter! So that's why I picked a fight with one of the night nurses over giving a patient apple juice!

"Your follicles don't look too great," Dr. Nyall said. To avoid looking directly at me, she stared intently at the screen of the sonogram machine.

"How many do I have? From the pain I'm having it feels like I have a million." (No matter what anyone said about ovulation being a chemical, not a physical, phenomenon, I swear I could feel each little follicle bubbling out of my ovaries. It was like a giant Alka-Seltzer exploding inside my pelvis.)

"You have four, but they're little. It looks like you're having a natural cycle instead of an induced cycle."

"But I'm taking mega-doses of the drugs! How can that be?"

"You have a primary follicle and four little secondary ones that aren't maturing appropriately. It resembles a natural cycle more than an induced cycle."

"So what do you suggest?"

"I'd suggest re-eval—"

"No, Dr. Nyall, just do it. *Please*. Just do the IVF. Use the primary follicle and one of the bigger ones. Please. I can't stand it."

"I'm very sorry, Sarah," she said. "It would be a waste of your time to do this cycle. Let's try again next cycle and see."

"No, I'm going to give up."

"Oh, don't give up, Sarah. Let's keep trying."

"Nope. I'm broke and worn out and the hormones are making me crazy. I can't do it any more."

Six months later, in office hours, I saw a patient for a new Ob appointment. She was forty-two. She was four and a half weeks pregnant.

"I know I'm high risk," she said apologetically. "But I really want midwives to take care of me."

"How are you high risk?" I inquired.

"Well, my age, and—and this pregnancy was the result of IVF."

"Really? Congratulations."

"Yeah, this was going to be my last cycle no matter what."

"How many did you do?"

"This was my seventh."

I sent her to the exam room, excused myself and went into the bathroom. I sat on the toilet and cried. I was so relieved not to be going through this any more, yet—what if I had continued for five more cycles? Would I have gotten pregnant? What if I had? What if I had and miscarried, or got a bad amnio result? All that time and effort and money, money, money—the vacations I didn't take, the clothes I didn't buy, the getting up at 4 a.m. three days a week, dragging myself to Dr. Nyall's office before it was light out, giving myself injections in the bathroom at the movies, in a moving car, in the on-call room at the hospital. What would it have been for?

And what if I had been successful, and had a kid to support on my income alone, with no one there to help when the kid vomited all night, or screamed nonstop for four hours with colic, or spiked a fever of 104 degrees?

I pictured myself dragging a heavy stroller down the subway stairs, rushing to get the kid to day care by 6:15 a.m. so I could start work at 7 a.m. What if I was in the hospital all night with a patient? Who would care for the kid? Who would kiss her goodnight and read her "Goodnight Moon"? And how much would someone charge for that service?

Was God trying to tell me something?

That night, as I lay on my sofa drinking the remnants of a bottle of wine, the phone rang.

It's Moe. She's going to tell me she's pregnant.

I got these weird voices in my head sometimes, not *voices*, as in schizophrenia, but my own calm, expressionless voice, out of the blue, anticipating the near future in precise events. I usually got these visions about patients: "Eileen G's going to call me tonight and tell me her water broke," or

"I'm going to deliver so-and-so on her due date," or "So-and-so's going to have a cesarean."

This time it was about Moe.

"Sarah?"

"Yeah, Maureen, what's up?"

"I have something to tell you."

"You're pregnant."

"What? How did you know that? I just found out."

"I had a premonition."

"Oh, God. You're twisted. You'd better stop doing that."

"I can't help it. It's a gift. So, how many weeks?"

"About five."

"So, what are you going to do?" I envisioned myself going with her to the abortion place. We'd both have to request the same day off, or one of us would have to take a sick day.

"I – I – I think I'm going to have it."

"The baby?"

"Yes. I'm going to have the baby. Will you take care of me?"

"You mean, like, deliver you? Of course." My mind was racing.

"But, Moe, I thought you …"

"Didn't want a kid, ever, right? I mean, I thought so too. Is this okay for you? Can you bear this?"

"Of course I can bear it. It's not about me, anyway."

"So can you do my first exam tomorrow?"

"God, Moe, you're not going to be one of those neurotic patients who comes for a first visit when it's still a ball of cells, are you?"

One of the attending physicians at our hospital, Dr. Nathan, used to tell her patients when they asked her too many questions at the first visit:

When you have more than eight cells, you can ask me that.

"What do you mean?" Moe asked.

"You know. They come to the office for their first visit when they're, like, four days pregnant—when it's still a *morula**—because they think nothing bad will happen if they do that. Can't you wait until you're eight weeks?"

"Are you going to make fun of me now?"

"Of course not. What do you mean?"

"Because, really, Sarah—I just want to be a pregnant woman. I don't want to be a midwife for this pregnancy. You know what I mean? I just want to be a pregnant woman. So can you do my exam tomorrow, please?"

* morula (mor´-u-lah) a solid mass of cells (blastomeres) resembling a mulberry, formed by cleavage of a fertilized ovum.

These Things Happen

"I don't believe you."

My patient, Abby J., 39 years old, 41 1/2 weeks pregnant, was crying, snot and tears intermingled on her pale face.

"I don't understand, Abby. What don't you believe?"

"You. Any of you. You're trying to force me into unnecessary interventions. Interventions lead to other interventions."

Things were rapidly going south. Abby, my patient for the past seven months, had gone for a sonogram for "post-dates surveillance" [when the pregnancy continues for a week or more beyond the due date, to evaluate the health and well-being of the fetus and placenta], and had been found to have low amniotic fluid [the "water" surrounding the baby].

Low amniotic fluid, or *oligohydramnios*, was a "soft sign" that the baby needed to be delivered.

It meant the placenta was not functioning as robustly as it should. It meant the umbilical cord was vulnerable to injury or accident.

Abby had been advised to have her labor induced.

Now we were into Day Two of the induction. She had had the "cervical ripening" phase the night before, in which a small tampon infused with hormones in placed in the vagina for 12 hours to make the cervix more "favorable" for induction.

It was 7:45 a.m. I had an IV bag in my hand with Pitocin added to it and was trying to persuade Abby to undergo Part Two of the induction.

Abby picked up a heavy paperback book with a diagram of a pregnant belly on the cover. I had heard of this book. It was called, "What to Reject When You're Expecting."

"What to Reject" was written by a lay person, a journalist, whose credentials included having had two home births. That was, apparently, what gave her the authority to write this book. The book had been reviewed on "Oprah" and its author, Harriet Ganci, was viewed by many as the savior of modern-day pregnant women. But its negative comments—which were many— were mostly reserved for doctors.

"Look what it says here," Abby opened the book to a dog-eared page.

" 'Doctors will routinely advise you to have your labor induced because it may be convenient for them. Don't be fooled into thinking this is better for you! Inducing labor for no reason commonly leads to cesarean section.' "

"Abby. Wait a sec. I'm not a doctor, right? You know me, right? And this induction is not 'for no reason.'"

The day was just beginning, and already I was completely drained.

"But you're doing what she says I shouldn't let you do! I'm going to end up with a c-section, I just know it!"

"Wait a minute, Abby. We talked about this yesterday. We agreed that having to have your labor induced because of low amniotic fluid definitely increases your risk of a c-section. But we all want a good baby, right?"

"My baby is just fine. I know he's okay. I think I'm going to go home."

"Whoa, Abby. Let's talk about this. When did we become the enemy here? We're not happy about this either. But we all want a good baby. Low fluid is a sign that the baby needs to come out."

"I know my baby is fine! You're trying to induce me because you're afraid I'll sue you!"

Abby was a lawyer who negotiated commercial real estate deals. She had seemed, from our very first meeting, sweet and passive, willing to put her trust in us. As recently as a week ago she had told Susan, "I really don't care if I have a c-section."

So where was this coming from?

I took the copy of "What to Reject" from Abby's hands and opened it to the chapter on "Avoiding Cesarean Birth."

"Look, here, Abby. She says, 'Choose a care provider who is sensitive to your emotional and psychological needs. This will probably be a midwife. The medical model views giving birth as a surgical procedure.' "

"But you're making me undergo an unnecessary induction. Unnecessary inductions lead to unnecessary c-sections!"

I turned to the chapter on "Induction of Labor." Under the heading, "low amniotic fluid," Harriet Ganci had written:

> "Your doctor may try to tell you that low amniotic fluid is a sign of placental aging or fetal distress. This is not strictly true. You may simply be suffering from a mild case of dehydration. Studies have shown that hydrating the mother improves the level of amniotic fluid overnight. Check out of the hospital, go home and drink fluids!"

Why not just let her go home? What was I afraid of?

But what if the baby died? What then?

Good babies don't go bad. Not usually. But is this a good baby? What about a cord accident?

My mind was racing. I was clammy. I thought I might faint.

"Abby, don't make me beg you."

"Beg me?"

"I am begging you to stay and let us induce your labor. I can't take responsibility for what might happen if you leave."

"I'll take the responsibility! I said that already."

Her husband walked into the room carrying two pillows and a duffel bag. He was a quiet, sweet, mousy man with hair plugs and a wandering left eye.

"Okay, fine. Leave if you must. But when are you coming back?"

"I'll come back when I'm in labor."

"But, Abby, what if you don't go into labor? How long are you going to wait?"

"Abby, what are you saying?" Henry asked. "I thought you were going to be induced today."

"I've changed my mind. They're trying to force me into an unnecessary intervention."

"Henry, can you talk to her?" I pleaded with him. "The baby is giving us a sign that he needs to be delivered. But Abby prefers to take advice from some poisonous book written by somebody with absolutely no credentials, instead of trusting the midwives she's been working with for nearly nine months."

I recognized a distinct whine in my voice, as though I was about to cry. It was unprofessional, what I had just said. But it was true.

Why me? Why couldn't someone else be on call today? Why did I have to be the bad guy again? Why not Susan or Moe? It wasn't fair.

"Why don't you let us talk for a little while," Henry suggested.

I was glad for the chance to get out from under Abby's withering stare. It was as though she'd gone from reasonable and normal to paranoid and accusatory overnight. What had brought this on?

Was I crazy? Why was it so important to make her stay and be induced if she didn't want to? Was I truly afraid the baby would die? I mean, how bad was it, to have low fluid? Didn't lots of women used to have low fluid before we had ultrasound and we never even know about it and they did fine?

On the other hand, didn't a lot more babies used to die in utero?

I thought of Lucien. I stumbled into the locker room. I was sweating.

I threw up.

"Okay, we're going to have the induction," Henry said cheerfully, coming out to the nurses' station to find me. I was frantically chewing cinnamon-flavored gum to cover the taste of vomit.

"We're sure?"

"We're sure."

Twelve hours into Abby's induced labor, she was four centimeters dilated. She had not had a great response to Pitocin, and it was taking loads of it to keep her in a decent contraction pattern. All day long, every time I went to the infusion pump to turn up the Pitocin a notch, Abby would attack me:

"*Again?* You're going up *again*? How do you know you're not giving me too much?

Or:

"I'm getting *enough* Pitocin! Why are you turning it up again?"

Or:

"Are you trying to kill me?" (I loved that one. *Yes, I am trying to kill you, because I hate you. I hate all pregnant women. That is why I became a midwife, so I could torture and kill pregnant women. Low pay? Long hours? Yeah, but you get to stay up all night and hurt pregnant women! What's not to like?*)

I had explained patiently to Abby that the body acclimated to a certain dosage of Pitocin and that typically, we had to keep increasing it throughout the labor until we reached a critical level, and that this level was different for all women. This did not satisfy her.

"*Again?*"

> *Ladies and Gentlemen:*
> *Now playing the role of Satan —*
> *Sarah Porter!*

By this time, Abby had an epidural—the old-fashioned, Dr. Wallace variety—and was supposed to be resting. It was more therapeutic for her, it seemed, to challenge me every time I turned up the infusion than it was for her to sleep.

"Abby, I already explained this," I said, sighing. I really did feel like killing her. *Can't you think about me, for God's sake?* I wanted to scream. *You've been torturing me since 7 o'clock this morning! I'm exhausted! Give it a rest!*

I had tried hard to appease Abby before the epidural, letting her crawl on the floor during the early part of her labor. The nurse was somewhat taken aback by Abby's insistence on being off the fetal monitor, as dictated by Harriet Ganci:

"If your labor is induced, your doctor will undoubtedly tell you that you need *continuous fetal monitoring* to ensure the baby's safety. This is nonsense. You need to move around, adopting physiologically sound positions, and listening to your body. Don't get trapped in bed!"

Abby's physiologically sound positions required me to be on my hands and knees for about three hours, holding the monitor on her belly while she crawled around, moaning and barking criticisms at me. My knees were on fire.

I couldn't get her hot water bottle to the right temperature, no matter how long I let the water run.

"*It's lukewarm!*" she spat after I placed the bottle on her back for the third time. She was crouching on the floor in front of the bathroom. The monitor would not reach this far. Annie, the nurse, was rolling her eyes at me.

Finally, in desperation, I tossed the whole nasty thing into the microwave in the nurses' lounge. There was half a stack of Ritz crackers lying on the table. I stuffed four into my mouth at once.

How long since I had eaten? I was ravenous.

The microwave was a very bad idea. At the very least, microwaving the rubber bottle was ill advised. The heat seemed to denature the proteins in the rubber casing. The thing now smelled like a giant pile of vomit.

"The smell of that thing is making me sick!"

Abby's bad temper persisted, despite generous doses of anesthesia in the epidural catheter.

"Hand me my book," she snapped at Henry. It was 8 p.m.

"Here! See?" she began badgering me again, quoting from Harriet Ganci:

"If you are persuaded to have your labor induced, you will surely need an epidural at some point, probably relatively early in the labor. Try to hold out! The epidural is yet another artificial intervention leading youdown the slippery slope to a cesarean birth."

I decided not to point out that it was Abby who had demanded the epidural when she was two centimeters dilated. Everything was really, finally, my fault—the low amniotic fluid, the induced labor, the painfulness of the contractions leading to the decision to get an epidural.

Henry smiled at me sweetly. I was going to kill Harriet Ganci, too, the first chance I got. Maybe I'd send her anonymous, threatening notes, with individual letters clipped out of magazines and glued onto shirt cardboard, full of misspellings and grammatical errors to throw the FBI off the trail:

Be*ee*-o**t**c**h**!

y**O**ⓤr a **Mo**R**o**N

d⊙**N**t *wR*/*T*E N**O**

m**R**E b**O**O**K**s or—

Yo**U**R Go/N T**O** EAT L**E**A**D**

By 10 p.m., Abby had progressed to six centimeters. The baby's head remained high in the pelvis. I remembered examining Abby at her first visit, seven months earlier, feeling her heavy pelvic bones, her forward-jutting *sacrum* and *coccyx*, noticing the tightness of her outer pelvic bones around my hand, and thinking, "this one's going to end up with a section."

Did I do this to her? Or was it just bad luck?

Finally, at 12:30 a.m., I told her.

"Abby, you're still six centimeters. It's called an *arrest of dilatation*. The cervix won't budge and the head is still high. The baby's heart rate is starting to creep up slightly. We need to prepare you for a cesarean section."

"*I told you!*" Abby screamed. Tears began to course down her chubby little cheeks. "This is *your* fault! I didn't want any of this! I *refuse* this! Get out of my room!"

"Abby, what are you talking about? This is not my fault. This is just bad luck. We knew there was a risk—"

"It *is* your fault. You forced me into an unnecessary induction, and you rushed me through my labor —you kept going even though I wasn't ready to move on to the next phase—you tortured me! You made it so I had to get an epidural too early, and now you're trying to force me into an unnecessary c-section! Well, I *refuse*! Now get out! *You're fired!*"

"Honey, what are you saying?" Henry jumped up and went to the bed.

"I mean it! I want her out of here! I want a second opinion!"

I walked out. I could hear bits of her waspish monologue as I walked towards the nurses' station: "... *forced* me ... I *told* her ... *sadistic!*"

"Jeez, Sarah." Jackie, one of the second-year Ob residents, was lurking in the hallway. "What's going on with your patient?"

"She's refusing a c-section, she has a fetal tachycardia [increase in the fetus' baseline heart rate above the normal range, suggesting infection], and she's arrested at 6 cms. And it's my fault. But other than that, everything's great!"

"God," Jackie said, "where do you find these patients?"

"Jackie," I pointed out, "*they* find *us*. It's not like we go out into the streets with sandwich signs saying, 'If you're unstable, entitled and paranoid-delusional, we're the midwives for you!' Right? *They* find *us*."

Mark Halpern, my consulting attending, was not happy. He did not like being awakened in the middle of the night, and he would readily admit this—rather sheepishly—during daylight hours (*But you're an Ob/Gyn!* I used to say incredulously, when he made this same weak apology the day after verbally abusing me on the phone. *Why didn't you go into Derm or Radiology if you don't like being woken up in the middle of the night?*)

"Can't you get the House attending to see her?"

"Mark, she wants a second opinion. She's gone all paranoid. She won't let me come into the room. She's lost her mind. What am I supposed to do?"

Mark was relieved.

"Well, I can't be the second opinion, because I work with you. It's —a—like a conflict of interest, or something. Who's covering the house tonight?"

"Dr. Covington."

"Okay. I'll page her and ask her to see the patient."

Abby finally agreed to a c-section with Marilyn Covington, the tall, beautiful, dreadlocked, soft-spoken Jamaican-born house attending, at 4:30 a.m. I got this information secondhand, as I was no longer permitted to enter Abby's room. I sat at the nurses' station reading a day-old *Daily Banner* until we got the word.

"Sarah. Why don't you go home now?" Marilyn was patting my shoulder.

I had fallen asleep with my head on the newspaper. I was drooling slightly.

"What time is it?"

"It's about 6. The baby's out. He's fine. Everybody's fine. Go home."

"Marilyn, how can I thank you for this?"

"Don't mention it," she said. "These things happen. Don't worry about it."

"Why do you personalize these things?" (Dr. Singer)

"What do you mean?"

"Clearly, Abby has a problem that has nothing to do with you. Why do you insist on making it personal?"

"I don't know, Dr. Singer; maybe it has something to do with being verbally abused for 18 hours straight, called a she-devil, and then not being allowed to take care of her any more. She *rejected* me."

"She didn't reject *you*, Sarah. It's not about you. You didn't do anything wrong."

"Maybe it's childish. Maybe I'm just tired all the time and I'm incapable of being an adult about it. But it's hard to do the same thing day after day and know that at any moment, for no reason at all, someone can accuse you of being incompetent and a bad person, just because things don't go their way."

"Have you thought about another career?"

"Oh, sure. I think I'll become a criminal defense lawyer! I mean, Jeez, Dr. Singer, I'm almost forty-one years old. This is all I know how to do any more."

"What about your journalism career?"

"The Banner? Yeah, right. I'll bet they're dying to hire an elderly midwife who hasn't edited copy in more than ten years."

"Well, Sarah, if you truly find this job too painful to do any more, and that seems to be what you're telling me, you have two choices. One, you can find a new career. Two, you can find a way to experience joy in what you do."

"Joy."

"You told me you used to feel joy. Remember? When you first started. You've shown me letters your patients wrote to you. You have found joy in this in the past. You need to get it back. Or find something else to do."

"Yeah, I need to have joy. But most of my patients are wonderful. I do find joy in caring for them. It's just the bad ones ... they really stick out somehow. It's like they weigh more than the good ones—the experiences do. The bad experiences are heavier than the good ones. They hurt my feelings. It's like we're not supposed to have any feelings. We're supposed to stay up all night, holding their hair while they vomit into a bedpan, but we're not allowed to have feelings. God, I'm whining."

"I think you need to articulate in your own mind what bothers you about this career, and what brings you joy. The question is, can you find a balance you can live with?"

"So that's my task?"

"That's your task."

Energy

"We just don't relate to your energy."

The speaker was Tanya, the partner of Dorothy, who had called me four times during the previous day to discuss her contractions. It was now 2:45 a.m., I had reluctantly admitted Dorothy to the hospital at 2 cms for pain relief, and she was snoring in the bed with an epidural to her eyeballs.

This left Tanya free to critique my energy.

"You don't relate to my energy," I said flatly.

This was a delaying tactic I had developed recently when tired or befuddled. If someone's statement or question didn't compute, I would repeat it, slowly, without emphasis on any single word, as a simple declarative sentence. This gave my brain a chance to reprocess the information, to make electricity, to synapse.

Susan used to scream at me when I did it to her: "Don't do that to me! I'm not stupid!" and I had to hastily reassure her that it was not she, but I, who was stupid. (This gets worse as you age.)

<u>We just don't relate to your energy.</u>

"I don't understand what you mean," I said stiffly. Dorothy continued to snore, great loud happy snorty snores that crescendoed and decrescendoed.

"We were hoping that Maureen or Susan would be on call for us."

I still didn't get it.

"But that's not going to happen. Whoever is on call for your delivery depends on the schedule. Today Susan has a vacation day, and Maureen is 30 weeks pregnant and taking limited call. I'm on until tomorrow morning."

I didn't tell them that Susan had taken an unexpected mental health day a week after she experienced a shoulder dystocia—one of the worst nightmares imaginable in obstetrics—and that her "energy" had probably been inexorably altered.

[A shoulder dystocia is an unexpected complication of obstetrics that occurs when a baby's head fits through the mother's pelvis and delivers, but one of the shoulders gets stuck behind the pelvic bones. Unless the situation is quickly corrected, the baby can die of asphyxiation. After a couple of minutes, Susan was able to deliver the baby with the help of one of the older attending physicians who happened to be walking by at the time. This man, a somewhat grumpy senior physician who didn't ever have much good to say about midwives, ran into the room in his Armani suit, threw on gloves and was able to rotate the baby inside the woman's pelvis and wrestle it out. The baby was stable in the N.I.C.U. and so far showed no evidence of brain damage, but she was having trouble moving her left arm, and would have to undergo physical therapy for a year or more. Whether she would ever have full use of her arm would remain a mystery for a long time. Susan had been crying and throwing up off and on for the past couple of days. She couldn't sleep unless she took Ativan, and she was talking about quitting. Moe and I were taking turns calling her and giving her pep talks.]

"So," Tanya said, sighing, "I guess we'll have to make the best of it."

I walked out and sat in the nurses' station. I was dying for a cup of tea.

As tired as I was, my brief conversation with Tanya had left me unsatisfied. What did she mean about my energy?

I walked back into the room. Tanya had turned the overhead lamp against the wall so that the light it made resembled a luminous small planet. The room was otherwise pitch dark. Dorothy continued to snort away, oblivious.

"What did you mean, about my energy?" I asked Tanya. "I can't work it out."

"I mean we just—Dorothy and me—just don't relate to it. Don't resonate with it."

My face was flushed. I squinted at her.

"Could you say it in English, please? What about my energy don't you resonate with?"

"I don't know. You just seem so *hyper* all the time."

"Oh, I see. You mean you don't like my *personality.* Oh, okay, I get it. My *personality.* Part of my genetic makeup. Shaped by forty-odd years on earth. Unlikely to change, unfortunately."

I left the room before Tanya could answer.

They didn't like me.

They didn't like my *personality.* They didn't like *me.* I had been kind and professional and patient with them for eight and a half months—they had started prenatal care about four days after Dorothy missed her period, before they even knew for sure that she was pregnant. I had seen them for their first visit and spent two whole hours with them, answering their endless questions cheerfully while patients who *liked my energy* waited, tapping their feet and rereading last month's "Lamaze Parent" magazine in the waiting room.

I had given them a tour of the Birthing Center when Dorothy was *seven weeks pregnant* instead of taking a lunch break; I had taken their panicked 3 a.m. phone call when she experienced spotting, and I had persuaded the sonography department to do a scan the very next day. I had reassured them repeatedly about the likelihood of their baby being normal, even when those panic attacks occurred well after business hours. I had reassured them about labor. I had reassured them about breastfeeding. I had reassured them about being parents. I had laughed and smiled and joked with them and rubbed their necks, and now I was going to deliver their baby.

They didn't like me.

They didn't like *me*.

They didn't *relate to my energy*.

They didn't *resonate with it*.

What should I do? Should I try to find some *wholly new energy* that was less offensive—say, someone else's borrowed energy? Should I simply deplete my body of energy—perhaps by staying up all night for several nights in a row, holding some laboring patient's hair while she vomited? Was *no energy* inherently less offensive than *too much energy*, which was, apparently, what I had? Or maybe the death of Lucien had permanently damaged my energy.

I wondered if doctors were subject to the same sort of scrutiny. I wondered if obstetricians' personalities got smeared on a microscope slide and analyzed and discussed by their patients. Or was this privilege—this permission to critique someone's personality—something that was exclusively granted to the patients of midwives?

Probably not.

Dorothy woke up suddenly at 4 a.m., demanding more epidural. She was six centimeters dilated.

The anesthesiologist injected a large bolus of anesthesia into her catheter while Tanya watched owlishly.

5:20 a.m. I had my face down on the desk at the nurses' station. Natalie walked by, out of breath.

"Your patient's having a decel. I'm going to tell them to set up the O.R."

In Dorothy's room, the fetal heart monitor was beeping, signifying a significant deceleration in the heart rate. I examined her. She was pouring bright-red blood from her vagina. Her belly was rock-hard. She was fully dilated, but the baby's head was high in the pelvis.

The baby's heartbeat stayed in the 60s and 70s [normal fetal heart rate range is 120-160 beats per minute] despite turning Dorothy from side to side to improve the blood flow to her uterus, increasing her IV fluid rate, stimulating the baby's scalp through the vagina and giving Dorothy oxygen by face mask.

Mark, my consultant, was home that night, at least 20 minutes away.

"Page the house physician, please, Nat," I said. "And page the chief. And get Anesthesia in here."

"What's going on?" Tanya asked. "We don't want any extraneous people in the room when Dorothy delivers. It's in our birth plan."

"Dorothy," I said, ignoring Tanya, "you're having what's called a *placental abruption*. The placenta is detaching itself from the uterine wall. That's why you're bleeding and the baby's heartbeat is decelerating. We need to do an emergency c-section right now."

"But we don't want a c-section," Dorothy said, starting to cry.

"Do you hear the baby's heart-rate?" I snapped. "We have to go *now*. We have no choice. It's an emergency!" On cue, the sleepy anesthesia resident appeared in the doorway and began asking Dorothy questions about her medical history. Natalie came with a foley catheter and said, "I'm goingtoputthiscatheterinyourbladdertocollectyoururineduringthec-section," as she jammed it in hastily.

Dorothy had fallen silent.

"Can't you call Susan to come in?" Tanya asked.

"This is not happening because of me," I said firmly. "This is an emergency. We have to go to the O.R. now. Do you understand?"

"But you said I'm fully dilated," Dorothy whimpered. "Can't I push?"

"You just received an epidural top-off," I said, trying to be patient. My hands were shaking as I shaved her pubic hair. "Your belly and legs are numb. The baby's head is high. We can't afford to risk his health. You could be pushing for hours. We have to get him out."

"What would happen to him if I pushed him out?" Dorothy said. "What do you mean, 'risk his health'?

"She means he could have brain damage," Natalie said.

Let's not sugar-coat it!

"He would not get enough oxygen to his brain," Natalie continued. "He needs to come out now."

She unplugged the bed, threw the IV bag on it and began pushing the bed through the door.

"Dorothy, do you understand?" I said. "Because if you do I need you to sign this consent form right now."

"You're taking me for an emergency c-section to save my baby's life?" She scribbled her signature on the form, the letters running downhill on the page.

"Yes, that's exactly right. You're probably going to have to go to sleep."

"But can Tanya be there? I want her there!"

"Not when it's an emergency like this."

The *fetal bradycardia* persisted in the O.R. Dorothy had to be put to sleep for the cesarean, which was a dire emergency by that time.

The house attending, Joe W., a young, enthusiastic, deeply tanned guy – one of the newer hires— and the lugubrious, overweight, Russian chief resident, Ivanna L., got the baby out two minutes after the skin incision. It reminded me of the good old days at NYCAS. The baby, miraculously, was okay. He cried weakly as they lifted him out of the incision, although he was pale and limp.

"He looks anemic to me," the Pediatric resident said. "We'll take him to the Observation Nursery and do a workup."

"It was a pretty good abruption," Joe W. said. "The placenta was almost completely separated."

Tanya was crying in the hall outside the O.R.

"The baby's okay, Tanya," I said warily. "It was a significant placental separation and he lost some blood but he'll be fine. He came out crying and he looks good."

"But I still don't understand. Why did we have to have a c-section if Dotty was fully dilated?"

"Tanya, the baby was in distress. He wasn't getting oxygen. The placenta was detaching from the uterine wall. Do you understand? It was an emergency. He could have had brain damage if we had waited any longer."

"What made this happen? Was it the Pitocin?"

"Tanya, she needed the Pitocin. When she wanted to get an epidural so early, we knew that she would probably need Pitocin because the IV and bedrest stopped the contractions. We talked about this. This is not anybody's fault. And Pitocin does not cause placental abruption as a rule."

"So what caused it?"

"I don't know. It's a mystery. Maybe the epidural lowered her blood pressure and there wasn't enough blood flow to the placenta."

"You didn't tell us beforehand that this was a risk of epidural."

God, was she trying to blame me for this? Her baby was alive and well and she was trying to blame me!

Dorothy cried when they gave her the baby to hold before they took him to the Nursery. I thought of Andrea Guarnaccia, after I resuscitated her baby, holding Lucia and crying and telling me I was a wonderful nurse.

That would never happen again. I missed that.

"Dorothy P. was too uptight to deliver vaginally," Susan said matter-of-factly when I told her the story later. "But are you okay?"

"Of course I'm okay," I said. "How're you?"

"Well, I'm a little better. I saw my therapist."

"You mean, *my* therapist? Dr. Singer?"

"Yeah, *my* therapist. I still see her from time to time."

"So are you giving up midwifery?"

"Naw," Susan said. "I don't really know how to do anything else."

"That's exactly what I told her. What did say?"

"Oh, Dr. Singer never tells me what to do. I just figured it out myself —that I needed to get back on the horse. But there's just one thing …"

"What?"

"It's your energy. It really bugs me."

"Oh, fuck off. And get back to work."

"Isn't it enough for you, to know that you did the right thing?" (Dr. Singer)

"But why can't they get it? Why can't they see that everything is not my fault? I'm doing the best I can."

"You know, Sarah, you can't change other people. You can only change your response to them."

"Dr. Singer," I said, "that's the first piece of actual advice you've given me. I'm going to try to remember that every day of my life."

Frank

"Oh, my God. Will you look at my ass, for Chrissake?"

Moe stood on a chair, her pants pulled down to her knees, pinching one naked butt-cheek between her thumb and pinky, shaking it back and forth. "Why did we ever install mirrors in the exam rooms?"

Moe was 34 weeks pregnant. She had gained 38 pounds already. She looked magnificent. The pregnancy had made her skin luminescent; her hair was thick and golden and wavy, her face was perpetually flushed and her body was powerful looking—huge breasts and a big, shelf-like stick-out butt. She was carrying what we midwives liked to call a "BFB"—big fucking baby.

"How big you think it is?"

"Honestly?"

"Honestly."

"I think it'll be over eight at term. Well over eight."

"Over eight! So that means if I go past my due date, it'll be, like, a big fucking whale! Some ugly mashed-up critter that I won't be able to push out. I'll have a horrendously long labor followed by a c-section. Oh God. Just *kill me now*!"

"Moe, you're Irish. This is your teleologic destiny! It would a waste of that massive gynecoid pelvis if you had a small baby, wouldn't it?"

She could not be consoled.

Moe was leaving the practice. She had cut back to 30 hours a week and we were interviewing midwives to take her place. Cynically, Susan and I secretly hoped to find somebody young, energetic and infertile. Our practice could not handle any more shake-ups.

Moe planned to stay with her mother in Connecticut for a month or so after the baby was born, until it got its first immunizations. Then she and the baby were going on the road with Barrington and So Jah Say.

My heart was breaking.

In the meantime, Moe was staying with me and taking part-time call. She had given up her apartment to save money; her cats had moved in with her mother, and most of her stuff had already been shipped to Connecticut. She was sleeping on my brand-new Jennifer convertible sofa—we joked about what would happen if she broke her water on it.

"There's something wrong with Frank," Moe said. Her voice sounded odd.

"What?" I was in the middle of office hours, and had at least three patients waiting plus one on the table, naked from the waist down, in stirrups.

Moe wouldn't call me in the middle of office hours for no reason.

"He has a lump on his back. I found it just now. It doesn't feel right."

"Well, what does it feel like?"

"I don't know. It's too hard to be a lipoma." [A *lipoma* is a benign fatty tumor.]

Frank was a fusty, neurotic, elderly half-Abyssinian cat that I had rescued from the streets of Washington Heights near the nursing home where I had first encountered Mr. Dupree and his hygiene/elimination activities long ago. On the way to the subway one afternoon, Moe and I had stopped at a bodega for beer, and there was Frank. Big, handsome, filthy and charismatic, he rubbed against our ankles obsessively, leaving a ring of dirt and greasy fur on our white polyester uniform trousers.

"He's beautiful," Moe said to the bodega owner. "Whose is he?"

"Nobody, Miss! Why you don't take him?"

"Take him, Sarah," Moe had advised.

"I already have a cat. Why don't *you* take him?"

"I already have two cats. You take him."

Frank was a high-maintenance pet. From the very beginning of our long relationship, each of his lives was clearly demarcated by the various health hazards he endured.

While working as a night nurse in Labor & Delivery at NYCAS, I was generally comatose on my time off. My apartment sometimes went uncleaned for weeks, taking on a fishy, ammonia-like odor, and I am ashamed to say that my cats may have experienced mild neglect during this period. Calvin, the under-cat, didn't seem to suffer much, but it was Frank's trademark to become insanely possessive of me at times when I wasn't emotionally available. Sometimes in those days I'd awaken from deep sleep, gasping for breath, dreaming of being buried alive, to find him sitting on my chest, his front paws nervously palpating my sternum, his gold-flecked green eyes staring at me unflinchingly.

"Are you okay?" he seemed to be asking. *"Is everything all right?"*

Sometimes after a particularly stressful night shift, I could barely find the energy to feed them. It must have been hard on Frank, to wait up all night for someone he loved neurotically, only to be ignored. He vomited a lot during that period, usually on the part of the sofa where I sat, or on the bluish Afghani rug that smelled vaguely of manure.

I noticed blood in his urine that Saturday morning many years ago—I remember it was Saturday because it was a holiday weekend, Memorial Day, and I was actually going to be off work for three whole days in a row—only because he had developed the habit of peeing in the bathtub, standing up like a dog, while I watched—his sexy, alpha-male way of greeting me when I staggered into the bathroom each morning.

I'd sit on the toilet, nodding off while reading old advertising circulars and sorting through coupons, and Frank would barge in, butting the door open with his head. He would stare at me pointedly, then jump into the dry bathtub and back his butt against the shower curtain, releasing an impressive stream as his bottom slowly rose in the air. Afterwards he'd glance at me sidelong, as if to say, *"What's happening?"*

That day, Frank peed pure blood.

The chapter on feline health problems in "The Complete Book of the Cat" was not encouraging:

<u>Signs of complete or partial urinary blockage:</u>

Straining to urinate
Blood in the urine
Restlessness
Sudden death

Sudden death?

"Animal Medical Center," I panted at the taxi driver, hoisting Frank onto the seat in his carrier. The bright sun of that late-May morning was blinding.

It was a partial blockage, and Frank survived.

"The radical treatment, if this recurs, is partial penile amputation," the vet said matter-of-factly, after giving me an envelope of antibiotics to administer to Frank.

"I beg your pardon?"

It was noon and I had been awake for 19 hours.

Frank was about 15 years old now, according to the vet's original estimate of his age.

He slept next to me in the bed every night, in the "husband spot," his head on the pillow, his body splayed out to make him look larger and occupy as much space as possible. This was to discourage Calvin from intruding on our marital bliss.

"I don't know what it is," the vet said, avoiding my eyes. "I have no idea. I'd have to biopsy it."

"But it doesn't feel right, does it?" I said, persistent.

"I couldn't say until I biopsied it."

Neither Moe nor I would say what we felt. The lump on Frank's back felt like cancer. I had felt cancer only two or three times in my career, and each time I had known instantly what it was. Dov had told me once that tumors, when incised in surgery, "cut like an unripe pear." That was what Frank's lump felt like.

Two years earlier, I had arrived home from a basketball game to find Frank missing. Ever negligent, I only noticed because Calvin came to the door to greet me—not his usual beta-male, self-effacing style—and gave me a beseeching look.

"Where's your brother?" I asked reflexively.

Frank was in the back of the winter-clothes closet, gasping for breath. His tongue, protruding from his open mouth, was grotesquely dry and sandpapery.

"We think Frank is suffering from Feline Allergic Bronchitis," the emergency vet said. "He's stable now, but we're going to admit him to the I.C.U. and put him in an oxygen cage. You can visit him tomorrow."

"Is he going to die?" I asked. It was 1 a.m. and I had been waiting in the freezing-cold lobby of the Animal Medical Center in my basketball shorts and sleeveless jersey for two hours.

"Honestly, we don't think so," she said. "We gave him some Lasix and Theophylline and he's breathing easier now."

The next day, when I visited Frank in the I.C.U., he climbed onto my chest and put his paws around my neck. This was a cat who, under normal circumstances, eschewed being held. He would approach and sit very near me, but I could not, under any circumstances, pick him up.

"He's probably hoping to sneak out with you when you leave," Moe said.

Saturday morning. The phone rang at 8:30 a.m. Moe, sleeping in the living room, answered.

"No, I'll take the message. Oh, I see. I see. Uh-huh. Yep. Okay. You're sure, then? Okay, I'll have her call you."

From the husband spot, Frank gazed at me sexily through half-closed eyes, as if to say, *Don't get up yet, baby. Stay with me awhile.*

"Who was it?" I called out to Moe. I could hear her hefting her considerable weight to a sitting position on the convertible bed.

"It was the vet."

"What did she say?"

"It looks like lymphoma." Moe stood in the doorway in her maternity pajamas. "They said to call them back and they'll refer him for chemo."

"Chemo?"

"Listen," the vet said on the phone, "It's the *best bad thing* he could have." I was given the number of a feline oncologist uptown. Frank, lying on his back in a cardboard box in the bright sunlight, chased his tail frantically while I talked to the vet.

There can't be anything wrong with him.

In his dotage, Frank suffered from constipation. I had caught him once a year or so earlier, straining so hard in the litter box that he farted musically. I had assumed it was another urinary blockage, and rushed him to the AMC again.

"See this?" the vet said, illuminating the X-ray light board for my benefit. "What do you see?"

"Is it … poo?"

"Impacted feces. Up to his tits," the vet said matter-of-factly. "He's totally constipated. He's getting an enema as we speak."

After that, Frank's daily life involved liquid laxative. Sometimes the constipation overwhelmed him, and the act of shitting, once taken for granted, would create annoying little klingons to bedevil him.

"We call them *campers* or *pirates*," my vet said on the phone, in a kindly voice. "It happens to older cats a lot. Some people call them *dingleberries*. Just do the best you can."

After a poop, Frank would sometimes run around the apartment in a frenzy, dragging his butt on the rug or the sofa, crying out in a tortured contratenor. I'd follow him around with rubber gloves and a gauze pad soaked in mineral oil, trying to calm him. When he was relaxed enough, I'd straddle him and "deliver" the miniature "baby" from his rectal sphincter. After all, I was a midwife. This was my job.

Dr. Davis, the feline oncology specialist, palpated Frank's lump, then examined him. He performed a chest X-ray and an abdominal ultrasound to rule out spread of the cancer. Frank was scheduled for excision biopsy and bone-marrow aspiration the following day with Dr. Breno. Dr.

Davis was cheerful and enthusiastic, advising me to pursue chemotherapy once the surgery was completed.

The lump, which hadn't existed two weeks before, was growing daily. Now it was about the circumference of a jacks ball, sticking up about a quarter of an inch, distorting the beautiful contours of Frank's back.

"You don't have to visit if you don't want to," Dr. Breno advised. "He's really pretty out of it."

The surgery had not gone well. The tumor had completely embedded itself in Frank's underlying tissue and muscle. Dr. Breno was unable to remove most of it.

When he saw me, Frank tried to stand up in his cage. His entire back was swaddled tightly in white bandages. His right paw was bandaged as well, to hold the IV in place. He purred loudly—not the subtle, contented purr I was accustomed to, but a ghastly death-rattle, loud, urgent, constant. Groggy, he fell over onto his side, lolling his head back to stare at me. He draped his good paw elegantly over the bandaged one.

Post-operatively, Frank was bald in places no cat should be hairless. Bald over half his back where they shaved him for the surgery, the stitches sticking up raggedly like a giant's whiskers along the curve of the incision. Bald on his belly where they shaved him for the ultrasound. Bald on his left shoulder where they trimmed the fur to place the narcotic patch for post-operative pain relief.

"The patch is activated by heat," the nurse warned me as I put Frank into his carrier. "Don't let him lie in the sun or near the heater."

Hello, people. He's a *cat*.

The first place Frank went when I got him home was the windowsill, in the sun, over the heater.

"He's stopped eating," Moe warned me two days later. I had worked 12 hours in Labor & Delivery and was nearly comatose.

"Can we force-feed him?"

The vet advised force-feeding Frank baby food with a syringe and giving him IV fluid under his skin with a large-bore needle. She thought he'd probably snap out of it.

Frank, weakened by his disease and the lingering effect of drugs, nevertheless fought like hell against the force-feedings and the fluids. It felt as though we were raping him.

He stopped bathing. Once obsessed with cleanliness, he neglected himself utterly, languishing on the sofa, hunched up, staring intently at me. This was a cat who used to bathe his tail alone for twenty minutes—he'd focus on a tiny, two-centimeter patch, lick it fifteen or so times and then move a millimeter to the right to continue the ritual. His morning bath used to take more than an hour.

"I don't like the way his breathing sounds," Dr. Davis said. "I'm reluctant to start chemo today."

That night, Moe sat on the sofa with Frank beside her and tried to brush him. He had very little hair left, but he loved a good brushing. He had begun to pee on himself when picked up. Dr. Davis had decided not to start chemo but to reevaluate in a day or two. I was trying to position Frank so that I could place the needle under his skin for the subcutaneous fluids.

"Sarah," Moe said, "take a look."

Frank's right pupil was completely dilated. He turned his head, on cue, and stared at me steadily with his left eye. Moe offered him a plate of vitamin paste and baby food mixed together. He sniffed it, then licked the edge of the plate wearily.

"His right pupil is blown," Moe said. "What does that mean?"

"I'd guess brain mets," I said. Probably the dilated pupil meant that the cancer had reached Frank's brain, had *metastasized*.

Frank jumped off the sofa, nearly falling over as he did so, and walked in rickety fashion towards the closet. This had become the only place he liked to be. His thigh muscles had completely atrophied, and the naked pink skin was stretched tight over his spine.

"We can insert a feeding tube today," Dr. Davis said, "and feed him that way until he's strong enough for chemo."

"Sarah?"

Moe nudged me. The vet was staring at me. Frank lay on his side on the table, purring the death-purr, exhausted.

"No," I said. "No feeding tube. He's a cat, for God's sake. He's fifteen years old."

I sat on a plastic chair in the exam room. Moe squatted on the floor next to me. Frank was in my lap on a towel, an IV catheter sticking out of his neck.

The evening before, Frank had started out in the closet, but when I woke up that morning he was on my bed in the husband spot, staring anxiously at me with his good left eye.

"Can't you help me?" he seemed to say.

He deliberately leaned what was left of his weight against me, as if trying to feel as much of me as he could with his ravaged little body.

Frank shivered violently. Moe scratched him under his chin and stroked his ears. She took my hand. The vet held the syringe, filled with pink liquid, waiting for my signal.

"Go ahead," I said.

Get Up, Stand Up

I am so deeply asleep that I attack the alarm clock for a minute or so until I realize it's the beeper, not the clock.

Please call Rosememe H.,
9 mos. preg in labor.

Rosememe is the person who I suspect has been sending me anonymous religious tracts in the mail, admonishing me to *Seek Jesus now!*

Rosememe is having her third baby. She is a tiny Haitian woman, a born-again Christian, with large piercing eyes and a perpetually sad expression.

Her husband, Leonid, is a cheerful, short, muscular man with prematurely graying hair who does not feel the need to proselytize; on the other hand, Rosememe does enough for two or three people.

"Do you know the love of Jesus?" she implores me urgently each time I greet her in the private practice office.

In the Triage room in Labor & Delivery, she is praying fervently in Creole when I walk in.

"Pwaise God!" she shouts when she sees me. It's rare that my arrival is heralded with such acclaim. Leonid smiles and shakes my hand.

"Jesu, Jesu, Jesu – 'ere is another one!" Rosememe arches her back on the exam table dramatically, her braids almost touching her lower back.

"Rosememe, take it easy," I say. It is almost 4 a.m.

Rosememe is 5 centimeters dilated.

"Pwaise Him! Pwaise his name!" she shouts hoarsely.

We make our slow way down the hall to the Birth Center, Rosememe praying continually as we walk. Walking with a woman in labor is something like walking with a two-year-old or a dog—it takes about four times longer than it should because of the need to stop every couple of feet.

Leonid, ever cheerful, hoists Rosememe's tattered bag. They are very poor, I suspect—Leonid works as a security guard in a fancy Upper East Side hotel; Rosememe stays home and cares for their children.

She paces around the birthing room frantically, her little butt protruding from the back of the gown. As the labor progresses she begins belching rhythmically, so that a passerby might imagine a Popeye-and-Bluto poker game going on inside, or an adolescent gross-out contest.

Standing at the foot of the bed, Rosememe vomits violently. Rosememe and Leonid are vegetarians. Inspired by my sensible advice to stay well nourished in early labor, Rosememe has recently consumed an entire meal.

The housekeeping guy is nervous in the presence of a pregnant woman in a peek-a-boo hospital gown who is pacing the floor. He cannot meet our eyes. He does a really poor job cleaning up.

Throughout the remainder of the labor, Leonid insists on pointing out various barfed-up ingredients on the floor that the housekeeping guy missed.

"Soba noodle!" he says emphatically, or, "fava bean!"

I am trying to comfort Rosememe, who has withdrawn inward, as many laboring women do. She is lying on the foot of the bed now, curled up. The room is almost completely dark. I am holding her hand and rubbing her arm. The sky is beginning to lighten. She is starting to make low grunting sounds. As her labor progresses, she speaks Creole almost exclusively. Sometimes she sings bits of Haitian lullabies:

Dodo, maringwen, dodo,
Dodo, maringwen, dodo,
Trois heur d'ouvant jou'
Bigail piquer mwen
Mwen pa connanin position
Mwen ve!
Dodo, maringwen, dodo.

Other times she sings hymns, in English for my benefit:
On a 'ill far away
Stood an old Wugged Cwoss
The emblem of suff'wing and shame ...

I happen to know this hymn. Although I was raised a Methodist, summers in my childhood were spent on my mother's parents' farm in southern Indiana. My maternal grandparents were evangelical Baptists.

I sing along:

And I love that old cross
Where the dearest and best
For a world of lost sinners was slain...

"*Jesu, Jesu! Tout moun pe ou!*" (Jesus, Jesus! All men fear you!)

Rosememe is bearing down involuntarily, so it sounds as though she is addressing Jesus while on the toilet.

"Red onion!" Leonid points to a spot on the floor near the bed.

"You're doing great, Rosememe. You're the best!"

"*Jesus* is the best!" Rosememe admonishes me, squeezing my hand stiffly. "*Jesu, Jesu!*"

"There's a white bean!"

"Are you starting to feel like pushing?"

"Praise Jesu! *M'vle pousse!*" (I want to push!)

"Eggplant!"

Rosememe begins pushing. It is 5:45.

She invokes Jesus' name operatically between contractions. Leonid continues relentlessly locating and identifying undigested food bits. The sky is a fantastic shade of pearl pink.

6:13 a.m.

"Baby girl!"

"*Mesi, Jesu, Mesi! Mesi, Jesu, Mesi! Mesi, Jesu, Mesi!* (Thank you, Jesus, thank you!) Sarah, do you know the love of Jesus?"

"Yes, I do."

"*All pwaise to Jesu!*"

The only light in the room is from the overhead delivery lamp. I hand the baby to Rosememe, who drapes her across her chest and murmurs to her in Creole about Jesus.

Peter Tosh is playing in the background on Leonid's tiny CD player:

Get up, stand up.
Stand up for your rights.
Get up, stand up.
Don't give up the fight.

The sun is coming up over New York Harbor, staining the clouds psychedelic pink and orange. The buildings of lower Manhattan appear to be on fire. There are crows nesting in the trees by the parking garage. Blue jays soar overhead, making their raucous, insistent, murderous sounds. The baby mews and coos on Rosememe's chest.

How long since I noticed this?

Joy

"So you're the one that's going to induce my labor," she said, glaring at me.

"Whoa, Ms. Cameron, let's start over," I said, backing away. "My name is Sarah Porter. I'm the midwife who's working in Labor & Delivery today. The nurse sent me in to start your admission. Why are we inducing your labor?"

She sighed, staring just past me into the hallway.

"I'm past my due date and they say my water's low." (The amniotic fluid level was diminished, similar to the case of Abby J., suggesting that the placenta was not functioning as robustly as it should and the baby would be better off out than in.)

"Okay, so let me examine you and see what we're starting from."

"I want to deliver squatting."

"I beg your pardon?"

"I want to deliver squatting. This book says it's more natural than laying on your back," she said, pulling out a large, thick paperback from her suitcase. "My first delivery was flat on my back and I didn't like it."

"Well, Joy," I said, "if you deliver on my time and the baby's okay, you can deliver any way you want to."

"Really?"

"Who's the patient you admitted?" Regina asked me at the nurses' station, flashing a toothpaste smile. Regina was one of three Ob/Gyn chief residents, in her fourth year of studying obstetrics and gynecology. At the end of this year, she would graduate and move on.

I couldn't wait. Regina, in addition to being falsely cheerful all the time, embodied what my colleague, Mark, called an unfortunate combination of ignorance and arrogance. A host of senior physicians had tried to correct Regina's many misconceptions about basic Ob precepts over the years. She could not be swayed. *All of you are wrong*, her expression always said.

I had witnessed attending physicians, their patience exhausted, shouting at Regina at the nurses' station or in the doctors' lounge, jabbing their fingers at the pages of an Ob textbook, trying desperately to get her to abandon an incorrect idea. When confronted with written evidence of her wrongness, Regina would simply shut down, assuming a blank expression and staring straight ahead. Her upper lip would curl slightly, Elvis-like, as though she was smelling something rotten.

"She's 41, a Para 1, sent from the clinic for induction for oligohydramnios at 41 weeks." I tried not to look directly at her.

"You started the Pitocin on her?"

"*Duh!* She's only been here for two hours. Yes, *of course* I started the Pitocin on her."

"Did you speak to the attending first?" A little frown of frustration distorted her pretty, blank features.

"Uh, *no*. She was a scheduled induction from the clinic. If the induction was scheduled by the clinic attending, it wouldn't require additional approval from Dr. Stewart, would it?"

I could feel my shoulders knotting up.

She gazed at me disapprovingly, as though disappointed by the naughty behavior of a spoiled child.

"I just think, Sarah, as a courtesy to the chief and the house attending, you might have let us know."

"Well, try spending a little time on the Labor floor, why don't you," I shot back. "I've been covering the floor by myself all morning. Where have you been?"

"You could always page me."

"But where were you? If you're the chief assigned to L&D today, why should I have to come looking for you?"

"I would appreciate being told about all the patients on the board as they get admitted."

"You're supposed to be here *helping* me. I'm busy *working*. I don't have time to hunt you down. Where were you anyway?"

Regina didn't answer, but stalked towards Joy's room. I scurried after her.

"Hello, Joy. Sarah tells me you are being induced today. My name is Dr. Barrows, and I am the chief resident on duty."

That pissed me off.

Her *name* was *not* "Dr. Barrows." Her *name* was Regina Barrows. Her *title* was "Doctor." (For God's sake, it's possible to make it clear immediately that you, the doctor, are a superior being by simply adding, "I am a doctor" after "my name is Regina Barrows.")

I was just "Sarah" and Joy was just "Joy," while Her Imperial Highness wasn't required to share her first name.

Joy didn't speak.

"Well, I'll let you rest for now," Regina said, after a long pause. "Let us know if we can do anything for you." She flashed her famous empty smile and turned for the door. I waited until I saw her go down the hall towards the doctors' lounge.

"How's it going, Joy?"

Joy's 15-year-old son Isaac, a quiet, smiling boy with chin-length dreadlocks, sat in the lounge chair by Joy's bed, holding her hand and rubbing her arm during contractions.

"Who is she again?"

"That's Regina Barrows, the chief resident."

"Is she your boss? She looks younger than you."

"Oh, no," I said quickly. "We work together."

"Does she have to be here when I deliver?"

"Not if everything's fine," I said.

"Because I prefer you."

I felt a presence behind me. Hassan, the Iranian medical student who was "shadowing" the Ob team at my hospital for two months as part of an exchange program, stood in the doorway, brandishing a suction catheter.

"Say-rah, what is thees?"

As a midwife, I have personally done so much for medical students' education over the years that I could probably commit mass murder today and still have enough points left to make it to heaven. I taught them to tie knots. I showed them how to start IVs. I let them deliver babies with me, and I forbore their annoying questions, their emotional immaturity and their shrill, energy-sucking anxiety. Sometimes I comforted them as they sobbed (this was usually only the female medical students) after some real or imagined humiliation at the hands of a hostile intern or chief resident.

The residents in our program were too burnt-out or put upon or exhausted or uncertain of their own abilities to deal with medical students most of the time. Because I had developed the annoying habit over a lifetime of actually meeting people's eyes, and because I had a kind face, students were naturally drawn to me. Hassan had attached himself to me like a barnacle.

I sighed deeply as Hassan held out the suction catheter for my perusal.

He was completely oblivious to Joy's presence, or that of her son at the bedside, or the fact that she was having a contraction as he approached. She could have been having a full-blown seizure and Hassan would not have noticed, so determined was he to identify the foreign object in his hand.

For a second-year medical student, Hassan's knowledge of basic obstetrics was impressive. He knew a great deal more than most of the American-educated students I was usually saddled with—third-year students who actually got to do things to patients, versus merely observing—but he was completely stymied by the abundance of equipment designed for delivering American babies. Labor & Delivery suites in Iran, apparently, consisted of a couple of stretchers, some metal clamps, a few cakes of soap and reusable gloves.

"What is thees?" was his favorite question, directed at me after he had picked up a mysterious object such as an *internal fetal scalp electrode* (a corkscrew-shaped wire screwed onto a baby's scalp to closely monitor its heartbeat in labor).

Sometimes I would catch him in a contemplative moment, when he didn't know he was being observed, rummaging through the bins in the Triage rooms, picking up a sterile swab or a weighted speculum or a sanitary napkin, pawing the package clumsily, then balancing it across his palm, staring at it as though waiting for an oracle.

Another ten hours of Hassan following me everywhere but into the toilet yawned before me, and I had to deal with Regina as well.

For God's sake, I wanted to scream. *I haven't even had a cup of coffee yet!*

I led him out of Joy's room.

I liked Hassan, despite his oddness. He kept coming in, day after day, oblivious to the snide comments the residents and nurses made about him, completely open to learning, embracing each day as a new experience. I hoped that medical school in Iran, unlike medical school in the States, wouldn't smash his enthusiasm flat.

By noon, Joy was contracting every two minutes or so. She made no sound, but tears streamed from her eyes.

"Joy, what's going on? If you're in pain, tell me and we'll get you an epidural."

"I never had none of this with Isaac."

"Where was Isaac born?"

"Sav-la-Mar, Jamaica."

"Well, Joy," I said, "I'm guessing they didn't use this technology back then in rural Jamaica. The epidural is a great method of pain relief when you're having an induced labor. It's not your fault that you needed to be induced, and you deserve some rest. You don't have to take the epidural, but it actually might make your labor better if you can relax and even sleep."

"I didn't need any of this before," Joy said again.

"Say-rah, what is … ?" Hassan had crept up behind me and was holding out a Balfour forcep blade, used to lift the baby's head up through the incision during a difficult c-section.

"*I'll tell you outside,*" I said pointedly. Joy was writhing in the bed, gripping the handrails with one hand and Isaac's arm with another.

"Jesus Christ, Hassan! You're like a human wedgie!"

"What is human wedgie?"

"Don't you get it? There's a time and a place for things. You can't just follow me around, asking questions whenever you feel like it. I am not here strictly for your education. I am mostly here to take care of patients."

"What you mean?"

"You have to respect patients' privacy and the—the intimacy of their experience! You can't just come barging in and demand to know what something is all the time!"

I stalked off to the nurses' lounge. I needed a cup of tea desperately.

Ten minutes later, as I passed Joy's room, I heard the familiar electronic click-click-click of an internal fetal scalp electrode. That was odd. I hated those things, and I rarely used them unless a baby seemed to be in trouble or we couldn't monitor the heartbeat adequately with the external monitor.

Joy was flat on her back, an oxygen mask strapped tightly to her face. An internal scalp electrode had been attached to the baby's head and an *internal uterine pressure catheter* was protruding from her vagina. That meant someone had ruptured her membranes artificially in order to place those items.

An internal uterine pressure catheter—IUPC—is a thick, semi-flexible hollow rubber tube placed inside the uterus, once the membranes are ruptured, through the vagina and cervix. It is used to measure the exact strength of contractions when the strength cannot be judged by *external palpation*. Although IUPCs were not popular because of the risk of infection introduced by the placement of a rubber tube in a germ-free uterus, they were handy if someone's labor was stalled. They were also useful if you thought you saw suspicious fetal heart-rate patterns and wanted to know the exact timing of the patterns in relation to contractions.

"What's all this?" I asked Joy.

Her voice was muffled through the green plastic oxygen mask.

"The other one came in and told me the baby's heartbeat was down and she needed to break my water and put those things on."

I shot a glance at the fetal monitoring strip. A few minutes back, there looked to have been *loss of contact* between the external monitor and the baby's heartbeat—a common occurrence in labor if, say, the baby moved significantly and the external ultrasound device couldn't pick up the beat for a minute or two. Ever optimistic, the external monitor would dutifully record the mother's heart rate—the next loudest sound it could find—until it located the baby's heartbeat again. Of course, the mother's heart rate was significantly lower than the fetus's.

"What the hell do you think you're doing?"

Regina was sitting in the doctors' lounge eating fruit cocktail off a patient lunch tray.

"What do you mean?"

"I go to ... take a *piss* for a couple of minutes and when I come back you've got my patient flat on her back with an FSE, IUPC and oxygen? You ruptured her membranes for no reason? What the hell are you doing?"

"There's no need to talk to me like that. The patient had a decel. Dr. Stewart wanted internals. And she has meconium."

Apparently the amniotic fluid was stained with *meconium*, the fetus' first bowel movement, which was a fairly common occurrence.

"So what? We see meconium-stained fluid all the time. And you know perfectly well that what you saw was loss of contact, not a decel. Are you an idiot? You know there's nothing wrong with that baby!"

"She has oligohydramnios. She had a decel, and she has meconium."

"Yeah, the fluid is low. So you go and rupture the membranes, so now she has no fluid at all. What is wrong with you? Why couldn't you come and get me?"

"Where were you, Sarah?" she looked at me accusingly. *"Why should I have to come looking for you?"*

"I was in the goddamn nurses' lounge having a cup of tea. You could have overhead-paged me."

"This patient is too high-risk for midwifery management," Regina said evenly. "I discussed it with Dr. Stewart already. How is she *your* patient, by the way? Did you follow her in the clinic? I didn't see your notes on her chart."

"She didn't come to the clinic on my day, okay? But she asked me to take care of her just now when I admitted her, and I told her I would. How is she high-risk?"

"She is of advanced maternal age, with no amnio, and she has oligohydramnios and meconium."

Regina meant that because Joy was over 35 years old and had opted not to have an amniocentesis to prove that her fetus didn't have a chromosomal abnormality, she was a high-risk patient.

"Bullshit!" My hands were trembling.

"You can still give her labor support if you want to," Regina said with a little smile.

"This is a fucking outrage," I said. I slammed the door of the doctors' lounge.

"Sayrah—" Hassan came at me, holding a large vaginal retractor in a cellophane wrapper.

"*Later!*" I waved him off and slammed into the locker room.

"Dr. Stewart, it's ridiculous. The woman has a beautiful tracing—Regina totally misrepresented the situation to you earlier—and now it looks to the patient as though I've abandoned her."

"Sarah. I would appreciate it if you would let Dr. Barrows do this delivery." I could hear the annoyance in Lorna Stewart's voice over the phone.

"But why? The patient wants to deliver in a squatting position. She asked me to take care of her specifically. She doesn't even like Regina, which certainly shows good judgment. Why can't I deliver her?"

"Just let Regina do this one," Dr. Stewart said. "You can provide labor support, of course."

I slammed the phone down. Hassan hovered over my left shoulder.

"Say—" he stopped himself when my hand went up stiffly.

"Hassan, please just don't ask me questions today. You can follow me around if you want, but write your questions down as we go and I'll answer them another day. Just watch and learn."

Hassan gulped and nodded. His eyes were almost popping out of his skull. I had never been this mean to him before.

Four hours later, in addition to the IUPC, fetal scalp electrode and the oxygen mask, Joy had an epidural and, because she couldn't pee with the epidural, the nurse had thoughtfully placed a foley catheter. So now Joy had tubes coming out of every orifice. She even had some artificial orifices.

I was ashamed to look her in the eye.

"Where have you been?"

"Joy, the res—Dr. Barrows has assumed responsibility for your care."

"But why? I asked you to take care of me."

"Dr. Barrows feels that with the low fluid and the meconium, the delivery is too high-risk for a midwife."

"Is that true?"

I sighed. "Dr. Stewart, who is the overall boss today, has sided with Reg— Dr. Barrows. She asked me to let Dr. Barrows deliver you. But I'll still be here in the room if you want me."

"Push, Joy, push!" Regina commanded her. The nurse, Lily, rolled her eyes at me. I was standing at the side of Joy's bed, flexing her head forward. Hassan stood nearby, idly examining a tube of Erythromycin eye ointment.

Joy lay on her back, her skinny legs flat against her abdomen. The oxygen mask was so tight that her skin plumped out between the elastic straps. The thick green plastic of the mask muffled her screams and moans. Isaac stood next to the bed, holding her hand, expressionless.

Regina put her index fingers into Joy's vagina and began moving them up and away from each other, then back down and together, in a U-shape, violently stretching the vaginal tissue. Joy writhed and arched her back, her hands waving helplessly in the air.

"What are you doing?" I hissed at her.

"I'm massaging her perineum!" Regina shot back.

"That's not perineal massage," I whispered. "You're hurting her. Take your fingers out of there!"

"I'm doing this delivery," Regina reminded me in a stage whisper.

"Push, Joy, come on! Keep pushing. Push-push-push-push-push!"

"How about we let the epidural wear off?" Lily asked. "Or how about you let her rest between the contractions? There's no contraction now. Let her rest!"

Just then, the fetal heart rate, which had been clicking along at a steady 130 to 140 beats per minute, took on the tempo of a waltz. Click … click… click. (pause) click … click …. click..

"Bradycardia," Regina said flatly. "Get me the vacuum."

If Hassan was blown away by a suction catheter, wait'll he got a load of the "Mityvac."

The Mityvac vacuum was a rubber cup attached to a suction machine, used to yank babies out in case of fetal distress during the late pushing stage, or if the mother was too exhausted to push any more. It resembled a miniature toilet plunger.

"Is the attending coming?"

Regina didn't answer. "Come on, Joy, push-push-push-push!"

I repeated: "Is Dr. Stewart coming?"

"I don't know," Regina said, staring at Joy's bottom. "Did you call her?"

The fetal heart-rate deceleration persisted.

"Stop making her push!" I screamed. "Joy, stop pushing. Breathe deeply. Just breathe the oxygen."

"You can't put on a vacuum without the attending present," I told Regina.

"So, call her then," she snapped. "This baby needs to be delivered now."

"This decel is happening because you were making her push nonstop. Let her rest. Let her breathe. Let the baby recover."

Lorna Stewart barged into the room, her face red and sweaty. She had white cakey deposits by the corners of her mouth—what Moe used to call "Maalox marks."

"Why didn't anybody call me?"

Regina looked up. "I don't know; Dr. Stewart, I told Sarah to call you. Sarah, didn't you call her?"

Lying bitch!

Lily brought in the vacuum.

"Push-push-push-*PUUUUSSSSH!*"   Regina screamed. "Come on, Joy! It's for your baby!"

She placed the suction cup on the baby's head. She administered local anesthesia with a syringe and cut a giant episiotomy. Stewart stood behind her and watched.

Yanking on the cup with all her might, Regina delivered Joy's baby girl.

Hassan's face was pale. He was sweating as he stood next to me. I could hear his musical nasal breathing.

Regina took the baby, whose body was grayish-purple, to the warming table and began rubbing her back.

"Call Peds!" she screamed at Lily. She was in a complete panic.

"What's wrong with my baby?" Joy demanded, lifting herself up on one elbow and peeling off the oxygen mask. "Why isn't she crying?"

"Just calm down, Regina," Stewart said. "Suction the baby and give her a little oxygen. She's pinking up right now."

The baby began mewling and moving its arms and legs.

"She's okay!" Regina yelled. "Where's Peds?"

"I called them well before the delivery," Lily said wearily. "They must have been delayed."

On cue, the pediatric resident arrived. By then the baby was pink and crying.

"You have a lot of fucking nerve," I said to Regina in the doctors' lounge. Lily had advised me to *let this one go*, but I could not. Two hours later, I was still enraged. I paced back and forth in front of the board where we wrote the patients' names and pertinent info.

"What are you talking about?"

"You raped that woman."

"Sarah, what the hell are you saying? She had a bradycardia, the baby needed to come out, I got it out."

"You're a fucking moron!" I was speaking in a high-pitched, breathless, hysterical tone and my hands were shaking. "It was an iatrogenic bradycardia, you idiot! None of that was necessary." [*Iatrogenic = caused by the physician.*]

"None of what?"

"The violence, screaming at her to push, reaming her vagina, the episiotomy, the vacuum. Why did you do that to her? She's just an ordinary Jamaican woman who wanted to deliver squatting. Now all she's going to remember is violence."

"I don't know what you're talking about, but I don't like your tone," Regina said, stalking out of the room. "I'll be taking this further."

"Sarah, Dr. Barrows has accused you of insubordination," Dr. Reich said.

Susan and I had been summoned to the chairman's office at 2 p.m. the day after Joy's delivery. I was in the middle of seeing patients in the Clinic, and Susan had come in from home for the "emergency meeting."

"What insubordination? I don't work for her! She's not my superior!" Susan kicked my ankle under the table.

"Sarah, I am very angry with you. It sounds like you were completely inappropriate with Dr. Barrows. She says you used profanity, she says you called her an idiot and a moron. Is that true?"

Actually, I wanted to say, *what I called her was* a fucking moron.

"Yes, I called her an idiot and a moron," I said, teeth clenched. "She *is* an idiot and a moron." My heart was pounding.

"Sarah, this is unacceptable. If you can't get along with the residents, then you can't work here. She also said you tried to take over care of a high-risk patient. She said you undermined her in front of the patient. Is that true?"

"She's so full of—of *it!* She's so *full of it!*" I shouted back. Susan put her hand on my arm and cut me off.

"Stop, Sarah. Just stop."

"No one's interested in my side of it, I guess," I spat out. "She butchered a patient for no reason at all! She misread the tracing, and she took over the patient's care against the patient's express wishes, and she butchered her! That woman just wanted to have a humane experience. Instead she'll remember nothing but screaming and violence. And for what?"

"Sarah, I don't appreciate your tone. Dr. Barrows did what she had to do. There was no violence. And she was right—the patient was too high-risk for a midwife to care for her."

"Oh, pullll-*eeeeze!*"

Susan grabbed my arm again. Her hand went to her mouth, as if to say, *stop talking right now.*

"I want you to formally apologize to Regina, in writing, and I want you to seriously think about your relationship with these residents. We have to get along here. If you can't get along, you can't work here ... Which brings me to another subject."

Susan glanced at me sideways for a minute.

"It has been decided that the midwives should not be delivering the clinic patients in Labor & Delivery."

"Why not?" Susan asked. Her hands were in her lap now, her fingers intertwined, her thumbs rapidly rotating around each other.

"It seems to us that the patients are too high-risk for midwifery care. It represents a liability. Also, the residents need those deliveries for their accreditation."

"But what are we supposed to—" I asked. Susan kicked me, then interrupted.

"Dr. Reich, what will the midwives do to earn their salaries?"

"It hasn't been determined yet. You may continue to staff the clinics, of course, and you can keep delivering your private patients here if you wish."

"But, Dr. Reich, you know we don't cover enough clinic sessions to equal 40 hours a week. How are we supposed to get paid?"

Susan's hand gripped my knee so hard under the table I almost gasped out loud.

"As I said, you are welcome to continue delivering your private patients here. But your place on the faculty has to be re-thought."

"You know good and well we cannot live on our private practice income alone," Susan said firmly, staring him down. "And if we're not on faculty, how can we use the office to see them?"

He was throwing us out.

"This new plan won't take effect until the first of the year," Reich said, his voice steady. "So you'll have plenty of time to figure out your new roles in relation to this hospital."

Big Adjustments

"So, are you and Susan trying to get your delivery privileges reinstated?" Dr. Singer asked.

I had not felt the need to see Dr. Singer on a regular basis for a few months, but recent events had sent me crawling back to her. I was drifting off on the velveteen sofa when her voice brought me back to consciousness. It was dark and hot in her office, and I had been up most of the night before with a patient in labor. The room smelled of damp clean laundry.

"It's not likely to happen," I said. "We contacted the State Attorney General's office and the New York State Midwifery Regulatory Commission. It seems we don't have any right to keep our jobs if the hospital doesn't want us to stay."

"Are you still thinking it's your fault?"

"No. We're pretty sure I'm just a scapegoat. It's pretty obvious it's for financial reasons."

"So are you looking for another job?"

"I don't know if I want to stay in midwifery," I said. "At least not in this country."

"So where would you go?"

"I'm not sure. The hospital in Haiti where I worked as a volunteer offered me a staff position as the director of high-risk Ob services. I could live in hospital housing for free and they'd pay me a decent stipend."

"But weren't you miserable there?"

"Not miserable, *per se*. Just physically uncomfortable all the time. I could probably adjust. Here I'm … spiritually uncomfortable."

I knew I should be expending more energy trying to find a job, but we were in limbo, and I was perpetually exhausted. Moe was due any day now, staying in my apartment, and we had private patients with due dates extending into the middle of the coming year, and Susan and I would either have to transfer all of them to another practice or stick around for all that time, jobless, just to deliver them. Also, it wasn't clear where we were going to see our patients, since we were being kicked off the faculty and the offices were for faculty use only. Reich had mumbled something about the hospital charging us rent.

Nothing was certain.

"So what's Susan going to do?"

"She's thinking of becoming a home care nurse. Easy hours, decent pay, every weekend off, no nights. And no beeper."

"Big adjustments," Dr. Singer said. "Anything else new?"

"I found out why Lucien died."

"Lucien?"

"The baby I thought I killed."

"When did this happen?"

"You know, September two years ago. That baby—"

"No, Sarah, I don't mean when did *that* happen. I know when that happened. I mean, when did you find out?"

"Martine called me last week. She wants to have another baby."

"How old is she now?"

"She's forty-one."

"So what caused the stillbirth?"

I noticed how Dr. Singer insisted on depersonalizing everything that had to do with Lucien whenever we talked about it. She referred to him as "the fetus" and his death as "the stillbirth."

"It turns out that Martine has an extremely rare condition called antiphospholipid antibody syndrome. It's like a kind of lupus, only different. It causes the mother to make clots that circulate to the placenta."

"So that's why the baby —" she caught herself "—the fetus died? From a blood clot?"

"Yeah. It causes the placenta to die, sort of. It's like a—like a heart attack of the placenta. The blood vessels are blocked. The baby asphyxiates."

I didn't kill him after all.

"Is it preventable?"

"Well, we don't know much about it. It seems that if we'd known about it we could have given her anticoagulants—blood thinners—during the pregnancy. But we didn't know."

"So, Sarah, you didn't cause that stillbirth. How does that make you feel?"

How does it make you feel, how does it make you feel, how does it make you feel?

Moe 2

We induced Moe's labor at 38 weeks and six days. I had absolutely no rational indication for a medical-type induction with Pitocin, and Mark, my consultant, would have none of it. But Moe was thoroughly sick of being pregnant, and she had an agenda that was based on Barrington's band's travel schedule. So she began taking herbal tinctures—blue and black cohosh —three times a day on a Wednesday, increasing the intervals to every hour by Friday. Those tinctures were believed to bring on contractions.

I had examined her in the office Wednesday and stripped her membranes.

Membrane stripping was something you could do that might bring on labor in a more "natural" way than most of the other things we did. If the cervix was somewhat dilated, you maneuvered your examining finger between the membranes inside the cervix and the cervix itself. (Imagine a water balloon distended with water inside a bot-

tle. It was like peeling the outer surface of the water balloon away from the lining of the bottle.) In
doing this, it was postulated, you released *prostaglandins*—specialized hormones involved with labor—causing cramping and sometimes full-blown
contractions.

I stripped Moe's membranes on Wednesday,
she took cohosh for three days straight, and by
Friday evening she was pretty crampy.

For the *piece de resistance*, Moe had taken castor
oil at noon on Friday. Castor oil, a powerful laxative, causes intense spasms of the colon as everything you have ever digested leaves your body in
the form of explosive diarrhea.

Prior to that, she had given herself a Fleet's
enema for two days in a row. Enemas were supposed to have the same properties as castor oil—
by causing spasms of the colon, prostaglandins
released by the gut would, in theory, circulate to
the uterus, causing the uterus to also spasm. This
sometimes made labor begin.

We had bought the castor oil and the Fleet's
enemas at my local drugstore the weekend before
in preparation for our three-day "midwife induction."

"I wonder how it must look to people?" Moe
had mused aloud as we roamed the aisle of the
Village Apothecary, brandishing our enemas and
laxatives. "Do you think people would think it
was kinky—I mean, *you giving a pregnant woman an enema*?"

"Listen," I said, even louder, "it's the West Village. And besides, *what two adult women choose to do in the privacy of their bathroom is their business!*"

Moe and I made popcorn and watched a made-for-TV movie about a blind woman who learned to ride a horse. I applied moxibustion (a wad of herbs that you light like a cigar and use to apply heat) to the acupuncture points that had to do with labor —Spleen 6, Gallbladder 21, her lower back. Moe kept jumping up without warning and running to the bathroom, the castor oil having done its job wonderfully well.

"A lotta bang for the buck," Moe commented, leaving the bathroom for the third time. "That was $3.99 well spent. My asshole is on fire."

By ten p.m., Moe's contractions had died down. She looked exhausted.

"It's time to close up shop," I said.

We each drank a glass of red wine. I pulled out the convertible sofabed—Moe was too great with child to attempt this by now—and settled her in before going to my room to sleep.

At 2:05 a.m. I was awakened by a familiar noise. It was a low moan, of someone in trouble or in pain.

It was Moe. She was standing in the doorway of my bedroom like a ghost, holding her dripping nightgown around her waist in a sodden little twist.

"My water broke," she pronounced grimly. "And I'm in labor."

"Examine me," she demanded, sprawled on the sofa holding her legs up. It was 3:30.

"Moe, we don't want to do too many exams now that your membranes are ruptured," I reminded her. She had a lot of bloody show already.

"Just check me! I want to know if I'm ready to go into the hospital. My mom had really fast labors," she insisted. Her hair was stuck to the sides of her face in wet little ringlets.

She was four centimeters dilated, and the cervix was stretchy and paper-thin. She must have been contracting through the night before her membranes ruptured. Rose, who lived on the Upper West Side, came in her car to get us. She drove like a maniac, even though I had advised her to drive very slowly, to waste time, to let the labor advance. As I repeatedly tell my patients in the office and the Clinic, labor with a first baby is about killing time.

By the time we got on the Brooklyn Bridge, Moe had begun singing operatically. She was on all fours in the back seat, and when a contraction came she would hum loudly, a medium-pitched, vibrating note, her lips slightly apart, crescendoeing and decrescendoeing as the contraction peaked, then tailed off. She would raise her right leg and her right arm at the same time, drawing little notes in the air with her fingers and bracing her self against the back seat. I sat in the front passenger-side seat craning my neck to watch her. Amniotic fluid dripped onto the seat.

"I'm sorry about your car, Rose," Moe said. "And your new sofa, Sarah," she added.

"Shut up and dilate," Rose said.

"Take this exit," I commanded Rose as we approached the turnoff from the bridge. Rose, fixated on the performance behind her, drove right by it.

"Or not," I said. "This other way is good too."

As we sped down Atlantic Avenue, Moe humming powerfully, various little bakeries and specialty stores began opening their shutters. It was November, but still warm: New York's famous, protracted Indian Summer.

In the parking garage, Moe bent forward, her arms wrapped around a pole, her head on her arms. She was mooing now and rotating her hips sexily. She cocked her head, winking one eye, and looked up at me.

"Ooooof, oooooooof, oooooooof," she said. "I feel like I have to take a shit."

Could she really be that lucky? Could she have zoomed through the *active phase of labor* in Rose's car?

"Let's go to the Birthing Center," Moe said, saluting the security guard as we passed him in the lobby. "I really feel like a jacuzzi!"

At 5:45, Moe was seven going on eight centimeters. The baby's head was deep in the pelvis, and she kept running to the toilet every time she had a contraction. Rose was busy filling the jacuzzi and testing the temperature with her elbow.

"Not one drop of shit!" Moe proclaimed triumphantly, coming out of the bathroom. "But I keep feeling like I have to doo-doo. This is going to be the cleanest delivery you ever did, Sarah." As a contraction came, she bowed her head and grasped the bed railings. "Ooooooooh – ah! Ooooooooh – ah! Ooooooooooh – ah!" she sang, wagging her butt. She was naked but for a sports bra. Connie, the nurse, kept trying to hear the fetal heartbeat with the doptone, but Moe was moving so much we had to beg her to stand still so we could hear the baby from time to time.

In the jacuzzi, Moe wrapped her eyes around my face, staring up at me like a little wounded animal certain of rescue. Her singing had gone up an octave, so that she was almost screaming now, and tears were coming out of her eyes. The baby's heartbeat, when we could get Moe to stay still, was strong and steady.

"Ooooooooooooooh—   OOOOOOOHHHH – EEEEEEEEEEE!"

"Moe," I said, "try making a lower noise."

"THIS IS THE ONLY NOISE I CAN MAKE RIGHT NOW!" she screamed, clutching the hand railings of the jacuzzi in a death grip. "I DON'T KNOW IF I CAN DO THIS ANY *MOOOOOOOOORRRRRRRRE!!"*

Rose peeled Moe's fingers off the railings. "Geez, Moe, aren't you supposed to relax?"

"YOU TRY RELAXING WITH A BURNING BOWLING BALL UP YOUR ASS!" Moe screamed back. "I NEED A FUCKING EPIDURAL, FOR

CHRISSAKE! WHAT WAS I THINKING OF? AHHHHHHHHHHHHH!"

"Moe, come back," I commanded her. "Focus. You're almost there. Get a grip. Look at me. Take a breath and make a mooing noise like this: *M NNNnnnNNHHHhhhNNMMmmmM MNNNNoooooOWWW"—*

I did my best cow impersonation. "Try that. Screaming isn't helping you. Try making that cow noise like you did in the car."

"Like this?" Obediently, Moe inhaled and let out a "*MMMMMMMMMMMnnnnnnnnnnnnMMM MMOOOOOOOHHHHHHhhhhhhhhMMMMMNNN NNNNNNEEEEEWWWWWW.*"

"That's really good, baby," Rose said. "Do that again!"

We three mooed as one. Rose rolled up her pants and stuck her left leg in the jacuzzi as she perched on the edge, rubbing Moe's shoulders. I sat on the birthing ball, staring into Moe's eyes and mimicking her sounds.

How could I give this up?

Sometimes, when a woman is pushing, the midwife will offer to let her feel her baby's head so she will know the end is near.

About 95 percent of the time, we get an emphatic, *No!*

But Moe wanted to feel her baby's head. I reached her hand down as the little hairy ball appeared at her perineum, and she touched it eagerly. A smile crept over her face. She massaged her baby's scalp.

"Come on, my baby," she whispered.

"Birth time: 7:14," Connie pronounced. It was almost completely dark in the room. Rose had raised the shades just enough that we could watch the sunrise.

"Take a look, Moe," Rose said. I held the dripping baby over Moe's belly. Moe, who had her eyes squeezed shut tightly, shouted, "I don't want to look! Just tell me it's over!"

"It's over, Moe," I said. "Take a look here."

She slowly opened her eyes and hitched herself up on her elbows. Her bangs were plastered to her forehead and one little wet tendril hung down her neck, wrapping around her throat.

"It's a girl!" Moe exclaimed. "It's a girl? I have a daughter? Oh, let me see her!"

I handed Moe's baby to her.

Lisa

Lisa B. was a freshman at a state college near Albany. She and her roommate had attended a keg party given by one of the local fraternities one snowy weekend in March. Lisa woke up in a dimly lit room that smelled of socks with one man on top of her and two others watching. She was pretty sure she had been drugged.

"They were big," Lisa said, "Two of them were on the junior varsity football team."

"Once I woke up and started fighting, they got really violent," Lisa said flatly. Her face had no expression.

The frat boys punched Lisa in the face, then tied her arms to the metal bed frame with towels and underwear and took turns raping her. Afterwards they left her tied and locked in the darkness. It wasn't until the rightful resident of the room, who was away for the night, got home the next morning that she was released.

Although Lisa identified the three boys clearly from photo arrays, the judge eventually found that the police had mishandled the original arrests and interrogations, and all three got off.

Lisa's parents, who were prominent academics in the City University system, brought her home when she found out she was pregnant.

I met Lisa's parents at a memorial service for my friend Rose's sister Margaret, who had been killed in the September 11 massacre. They asked me if I would take care of Lisa during the remainder of her pregnancy.

"It's going to be a biracial baby," Lisa told me in the exam room of our office. "The boys who raped me are white. The lady at the adoption agency told me that biracial babies automatically go into the 'hard to adopt' category."

Lisa never asked for anything, but I gave her my beeper number anyway, and told her to call me any time. This was something I never did, but Lisa was the kind of person who would never take advantage of anyone.

"I'll deliver the baby, Lisa," I told her. "You don't have to worry. It'll just be us and the nurse."

Lisa was afraid that being in labor would remind her of the gang rape. She was afraid of what she would do when that happened.

"The whole time after, I never cried," Lisa said now.

She didn't want to see the baby or even know what sex it was.

"I know you'll make it okay, Sarah," she said, staring intently into my eyes. I was sure the baby would have eyes like hers.

Lisa was three centimeters dilated when she came into Triage at noon, and she had been vomiting for two hours. She had ketones in her urine, which was tea-colored, and she looked terrible. I was not sure she would be able to deliver a baby through her vagina. This had been Lisa's first "sexual" experience, although, as I pointed out to her repeatedly, *rape has nothing to do with sex*.

"Give her an old-fashioned epidural," I advised the anesthesiologist. "I don't want her to feel anything."

I held Lisa in place, her back pushed out to the anesthesiology resident, while he searched for the right landmarks to place the needle. She sobbed quietly as they worked, making no sound, but her body shook so that the anesthesiology attending said, "I'm very sorry, but we can't continue unless you stop shaking."

Lisa's parents had told her they could not possibly be present for the delivery. They wanted her to keep the baby, but she would have none of it. None of her friends knew the circumstances; only that she was pregnant. She was going to tell them that the baby had been born dead. So she labored completely alone, except for me and Colleen, her nurse.

"This is a miracle, Lisa," I said, removing my glove. "You're fully dilated."

"What do I have to do now?" Lisa asked.

"You know what you have to do," I said. "We'll help you."

"Do I have to feel it?"

I asked Larry Holman, the anesthesiology resident, to top off Lisa's epidural so that she was numb again.

"How many centimeters is she now?" Larry asked.

"She's fully dilated."

"Are you kidding? Why do you want a top-off now? Don't you want it to wear off so she can feel to push?"

"Not in this case," I said. "This woman was gang raped. She doesn't want to feel anything. She doesn't know what will happen to her —what she will do—if she feels anything."

"But I can't top off someone who's fully dilated. She won't be able to push. She'll need a c-section for sure if I do that."

"We can instruct her to push. This is a special situation. I don't know what will happen to her if she feels the baby coming through her vagina. Please, just let me speak to your attending," I said.

"Come on, Lisa," Colleen said. "It's just like taking a shit. You can do this."

My plan to let Lisa push without feeling contractions was failing miserably. She had been pushing for more than an hour and the head had not budged.

"This is how you end it," I reminded her. "Soon it'll be over with and you can get back to your life."

Lisa was planning to go straight back to college once the baby was born, only not to the same school. She would attend a private all-women's college in Massachusetts starting in January.

Her face distorted grotesquely as she arched her back, throwing her legs out stiffly in front of her.

"Not that way, baby," Colleen said. "You're not going to deliver through your legs. Push in your bottom."

The epidural was wearing off.

"I can't do it!" she screamed. "Get off me! Get off me! I can't!" She sat up in bed, clawing the air with her fingers.

After two and a half hours, I called Mark, who had gone to bed early.

"I'm sorry, Mark," I said. "She just can't do it. We tried having her push while she was numb and that didn't work. Now the epidural's worn off and she's losing her mind. Every time she gets a contraction she screams and fights us off."

"Hi, I'm Dr. Halpern," Mark said, offering his hand to Lisa. It was almost eleven p.m.

"She just can't do it, Mark," I said.

"I can't do it, Mark," Lisa said, looking at him for the first time. "Please, help me. Please help me so I don't feel this any more."

Lisa's baby, a boy, was born by cesarean section at 11:22 p.m. He weighed almost nine pounds. The pediatricians, who had set up a warming table in the operating room next door, whisked the baby out immediately, but he had already begun to cry.

Mark began talking loudly to the resident at that moment, which almost covered the sound of the baby crying in the next room. I loved him for that.

"Do you want us to take him to the Nursery?" Dominick, my favorite Peds resident, was standing by the warmer.

The baby lay on a striped blanket kicking his fat little legs.

"Sure, but—" I stopped myself.

"What?"

"Can I hold him for a while?"

"Sure, but why?"

"Just in case she asks me about him later. So I have a memory of holding him and what he looked like and all."

"I don't see why not," Dominick said. "Just bring him up to the Nursery when you're done."

I swaddled the baby as Dominick watched.

"Wow, you're a good swaddler," Dominick said.

405

I sat in the nurses' station holding Lisa's baby on my lap.

What would I tell Lisa if she asked about him? I tried to memorize his face.

He was peaceful, this boy, who had been conceived in the most terrifying and violent of circumstances. He was serene and beautiful. He gazed at me knowingly. His eyes were huge and dark, like Lisa's, with long tangly eyelashes. He had a cleft in his chin and a high forehead. His hair was dark brown and thick. What was going to happen to him?

He stared at me as if he were about to speak.

"You look good with that baby, Sarah."

I glanced up. Natalie stood by the counter watching me.

"Right," I said.

"No, I mean it. You look good. Like he belongs to you."

I knew what she was going to say next.

"Why don't you adopt him, Sarah?"

"Please," I said, thinking, *Don't say that.*

"You look good with that baby, Sarah. I mean it. His beginning was so horrible. He needs you, and you need him."

I have always comforted myself by believing that things happen for a reason. Lately that facile comfort keeps being called into question.

If this baby was mean to be, what did it mean that Lisa had to suffer so much humiliation, pain and terror so that he would exist for me?

I hadn't suffered at all.

So much loss, so much pain.

Moe had lost Josh. Philip's family had lost him. Martine had lost Lucien. Rose had lost her sister Margaret. Lisa had forever lost her innocence, her trust in the decency of human beings.

I had lost nothing. Nothing bad had happened to me. Not *to me*.

I held him. I held him and looked at him. He stared back at me.

About the Author

Sally Urang has been writing for more than 20 years. After receiving a B.A. in English literature, Sally worked at the New York Times as an assistant editor, creating graphics, captions and headlines. In that capacity, she also wrote various articles for the daily newspaper, Sunday edition and special sections. After eight years, she left journalism to pursue a career as a midwife. She has been a midwife for 15 years and has delivered more than 1,000 babies, but her love of writing has never wavered. She has published her work in a variety of journals, including *Esquire* and *Ms.*, the *Journal of Nurse-Midwifery*, *The Female Patient*, *Medical Aspects of Human Sexuality* and *Institutional Investor*. She was a contributing author on *The New Good Housekeeping Family Health and Medical Guide* (Hearst Books). Her work has also been featured online in CBS Healthwatch, GymAmerica.com and MSN's Pregnancy and Childcare Multimedia Health Information Services.

She lives and works in New York City. *Playing Catch: A Midwife's Memoirs is her first novel.*

Printed in the United States
83532LV00001B/6/A

9 781420 876215